# T·H·E
# *Authoritative*
# CALVIN
## AND
# HOBBES

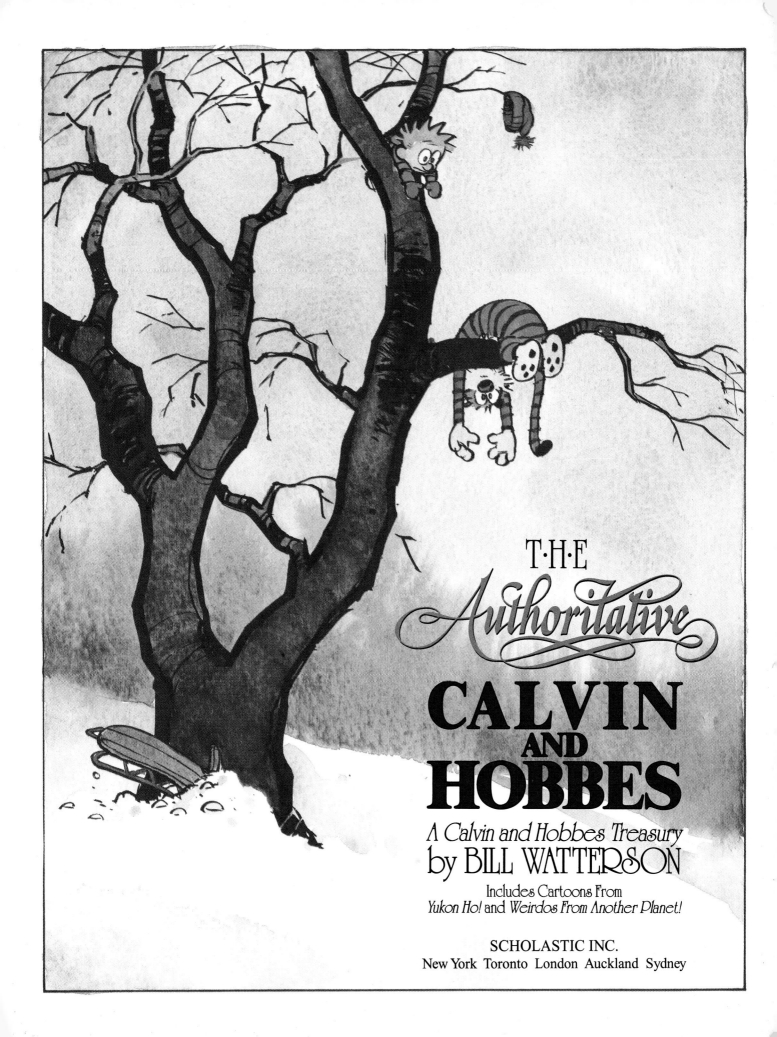

T·H·E

# *Authoritative*

# CALVIN
# AND
# HOBBES

*A Calvin and Hobbes Treasury*
by BILL WATTERSON

Includes Cartoons From
*Yukon Ho!* and *Weirdos From Another Planet!*

SCHOLASTIC INC.
New York Toronto London Auckland Sydney

*Calvin and Hobbes* is syndicated internationally by Universal Press Syndicate.

No part of this publication may be reproduced in whole or in part, or stored in a retrieval system, or transmitted in any form or by any means, electronic, mechanical, photocopying, recording, or otherwise, without written permission of the publisher. For information regarding permission, write to Andrews McMeel Publishing, a Universal Press Syndicate Company, 4520 Main Street, Kansas City, MO 64111.

ISBN 0-590-81923-2

12 11 10 9 8 7 6 5 4 3 2 1      8 9/9 0 1 2 3/0

Printed in the U.S.A.                    14
First Scholastic printing, September 1998

To Doctor Dave and
Fellow Moosers John, Brad, and The Frey

ARRGH! I'M **NEVER** GOING TO BE ABLE TO MEMORIZE ALL THESE DUMB VOCABULARY WORDS!

TRANSMOG-RIFIER

ZAP

TRANSMOG-RIFIER

HOW CAN ONE LITTLE KID MAKE SO MUCH NOISE?

WUMP WUMP WUM

**CALVIN**, WHAT ARE YOU DOING UP THERE?! YOU SOUND LIKE AN ELEPHANT! YOU'RE SUPPOSED TO BE DOING YOUR HOMEWORK!

CALVIN! MY, HOW YOU'VE GROWN SINCE I LAST SAW YOU!

I TRANSMOGRIFIED MYSELF TO FINISH MY HOMEWORK FASTER.

C'MON, LET'S FIND A MUD HOLE TO PLAY IN! ELEPHANTS LOVE MUD!

GREAT! YOU CAN TELL ME SOME ELEPHANT JOKES THERE!

HI CALVIN. BOY, LOOK AT YOU!

IMPRESSIVE, EH? HOW DID YOU EVEN RECOGNIZE ME?

I'LL ADMIT IT WASN'T EASY.

HEY, HERE'S A RIDDLE HOBBES MADE UP. WHO DO HOBBES AND I LOOK LIKE? CAN YOU GUESS?

I GIVE UP.

THE REPUBLICAN PARTY AND TAMMANY HALL! SEE? PRETTY GOOD, HUH? HA HA HA HA!

FORGET IT, HOBBES. POLITICAL HUMOR IS JUST TOO SOPHISTICATED FOR GIRLS.

HMPH. HER LOSS!

# Calvin and Hobbes

by Watterson

"BEFORE BEGINNING ANY HOME-PLUMBING REPAIR, MAKE SURE YOU POSSESS THE PROPER TOOLS FOR THE JOB."

---

"CHECK THE FOLLOWING LIST OF HANDY EXPLETIVES, AND SEE THAT YOU KNOW HOW TO USE THEM."

CALVIN WAKES UP ONE MORNING TO FIND HE NO LONGER EXISTS IN THE THIRD DIMENSION! HE IS **2-D**!

THINNER THAN A SHEET OF PAPER, CALVIN HAS NO SURFACE AREA ON THE BOTTOM OF HIS FEET! HE IS IMMOBILE!

---

ONLY BY "WAVING" HIS BODY CAN CALVIN CREATE ENOUGH FRICTION WITH THE GROUND TO MOVE!

HAVING WIDTH BUT NO THICKNESS, CALVIN IS VULNERABLE TO THE SLIGHTEST GUST OF WIND!

TO AVOID DRAFTS, HE TWISTS HIMSELF INTO A TUBE, AND ROLLS ACROSS THE FLOOR!

---

SOMEONE IS COMING! CALVIN QUICKLY STANDS UP STRAIGHT.

TURNING PERFECTLY SIDEWAYS, HE IS A NEARLY INVISIBLE VERTICAL LINE! NO ONE WILL NOTICE!

HEY DAD, KNOW WHY YOU DIDN'T SEE ME ALL MORNING?? I WAS TWO-DIMENSIONAL!

HMMM, I'LL BET YOU CAN'T DO IT ALL AFTERNOON, TOO...

DEAR!

I COULDN'T READ IT BECAUSE MY PARENTS FORGOT TO PAY THE GRAVITY BILL.

MAKE A PREDICTION, HOBBES.

WHAT FOR?

SO WE CAN SEE IF YOU HAVE ESP.

OK, I PREDICT YOU'LL FIND AN IRRESISTIBLE ATTRACTION TO A MUD HOLE.

!

HA HA. YOU STAY AWAY FROM ME.

IT'S GOING TO COME TRUE! I CAN FEEL IT!

HEY DAD, HOW DOES A CARBURETOR WORK?

I CAN'T TELL YOU.

WHY NOT?

IT'S A SECRET.

NO IT ISN'T! YOU JUST DON'T KNOW!

19

BOMBARDED BY HIGH-ENERGY PHOTONS, CALVIN IS TRANS-FORMED INTO A LIVING X-RAY!

ALTHOUGH THIS CONDITION WILL FACILITATE FUTURE MEDICAL DIAGNOSES, IT DOES MAKE CALVIN'S PRESENCE AT THE DINNER TABLE A DISGUSTING ORDEAL!

EVERYONE CAN SEE CALVIN'S FOOD BEING GROUND INTO MUSHY PULP AND SWALLOWED! AT THIS MOMENT, CALVIN CHEWS UP A LARGE SPOONFUL OF CREAMED CORN!

FOR GOSH SAKES, CLOSE YOUR MOUTH WHEN YOU CHEW!! YOU THINK WE WANT TO *SEE* THAT?!

MKGHH! SMACK! BLAGHKH!

HERE'S A LITTLE TOWN.

HERE'S A STEAMSHOVEL SCOOPING OUT A GIANT HOLE.

HERE COMES THE BULLDOZER, PUSHING THOUSANDS OF BARRELS OF TOXIC NUCLEAR WASTE INTO THE GIANT HOLE.

OVER THE YEARS, THESE DANGEROUS POISONS SEEP INTO UNDERGROUND WATERWAYS.

THE CANCER RATE OF THE NEARBY LITTLE TOWN TRIPLES.

IF YOU WANT ME, I'LL BE UNDER THE BED.

A STRIKE?? THAT PITCH WAS FOUR FEET ABOVE MY HEAD!

HA! IT WAS A *PERFECT* PITCH! YOU'RE JUST TOO SHORT!

YEAH? WELL, *YOU'RE* JUST TOO STUPID!

WELL, YOU'RE JUST TOO *UGLY!*

KICK KICK KICK KICK

KICK KICK KICK KICK KICK KICK KICK

KICKING DUST IS THE ONLY PART OF THIS GAME WE REALLY LIKE.

# CalviN and HobbEs
by WATTERSON

I'M GOING OUTSIDE, MOM!

HOLD ALL MY CALLS.

CALVIN LOOKS AROUND. SOMETHING IS DIFFERENT.

THE ODD-COLORED TREE BEHIND HIM SLOWLY LIFTS UP! IT'S NOT A TREE AT ALL! IT'S A LEG!

OH NO! CALVIN IS THE SIZE OF A BUG **TO** A BUG! HE RUNS FOR HIS LIFE!

A CLAW CRASHES WITH DEAFENING IMPACT! THE BUG IS TRYING TO STEP ON CALVIN! WHAT A HORRIBLE FATE!

CALVIN SCRAMBLES MADLY, PROMISING HIMSELF THAT HE'LL NEVER SQUISH ANOTHER BUG IF HE LIVES TO RETURN TO NORMAL SIZE!

SUDDENLY IN A SPRAY OF SLIME, THE BUG IS GONE! A MONSTROUS FROG LICKS ITS CHOPS! CALVIN IS SAVED!

AACCK! WHAT'S THAT ON MY PLATE?! GOOD HEAVENS, GET IT OFF THE TABLE.!!

BUT MOM, FROGS ARE OUR *FRIENDS*!

24

OK, I THINK THAT'S DAD'S BUILDING UP AHEAD.

I'M NOT SURE WHERE HIS OFFICE IS, SO WE'LL JUST HAVE TO LOOK IN THE WINDOWS AS WE ZIP BY.

HEY! THERE HE IS! THERE'S DAD! HI, DAD! DAD, LOOK! OUT THE WINDOW!!

DARN IT! HE'S STILL READING THAT BRIEF. LOOK OUT THE WINDOW, DAD!

DID YOU BRING ANY ROCKS? I DIDN'T THINK TO.

HEY DAD! LOOK OUT THE WINDOW! ...I CAN'T BELIEVE HE'S JUST SITTING IN THERE.

WHY DOESN'T HE LOOK UP?

I GUESS HE'S PRETTY BUSY.

YEAH, BUT WE CAN'T SIT UP HERE ALL DAY! SHEESH. LET'S GO.

IF HE HAD NOTICED US, WE COULD'VE GIVEN HIM A RIDE HOME.

HMPH. I SAY LET HIM TAKE THE SMELLY OL' BUS IF HE CAN'T EVEN LOOK OUT THE WINDOW ONCE IN A WHILE. SERVES HIM RIGHT.

I'M HOME!

DAD! HOBBES AND I FLEW BY YOUR OFFICE WINDOW TODAY ON A RUG! WE SAW YOU WORKING.

WE WAVED AND HOLLERED, BUT YOU DIDN'T EVEN LOOK UP. WE COULDN'T BELIEVE IT. YOU MISSED THE WHOLE THING!

I THOUGHT WE WERE CUTTING DOWN HIS SUGAR INTAKE.

26

# Calvin and Hobbes by WATTERSON

OY OH BOY OH BOY OH BOY OH BOY OH BOY OH BOY OH BOY OH BOY OH BOY

WAIT! WAIT! I'VE GOT TO SAVOR THIS MOMENT! THE BRILLIANCE OF IT ALL! I'M A GENIUS! A SHEER *GENIUS!*

SUSIE'S PLAYING ON THE SIDEWALK! NOW'S MY CHANCE TO USE THE SNOWBALL I'VE BEEN SAVING IN THE FREEZER!

SHE'LL NEVER EXPECT A SNOWBALL IN *JUNE!* BOY, WILL SHE BE MAD! HA HA HA!

THIS IS GOING TO BE GREAT! HERE IT COMES! OH BOY! OH BOY!

HEY SUSIE!! PIFF

I *MISSED!* DARN IT DARN IT DARN IT!! OF ALL THE MISERABLE LUCK! AAARRGHH!

THERE MUST'VE BEEN A CROSS BREEZE! I CAN'T BELIEVE IT! I SAVED THAT SNOWBALL FOR THREE WHOLE MONTHS! I...

SCOOP SCOOP

I.. I...UH...

POW

THE IRONY OF THIS IS JUST SICKENING.

1988 ISN'T TOO FAR AWAY, DAD.

IF YOU'RE THINKING OF RUNNING FOR "DAD" AGAIN, YOU'D BETTER GET YOUR CAMPAIGN IN GEAR.

FRANKLY, THE POLLS LOOK GRIM. I DON'T THINK YOU'VE GOT MUCH OF A SHOT AT KEEPING THE OFFICE.

I TAKE COMFORT IN THE FACT THAT NOT MANY PEOPLE WOULD WANT IT.

FLIPPANT REMARKS HAVE A WAY OF HAUNTING CANDIDATES, YOU KNOW.

THE CHAMELEON SITS MOTIONLESS.

AMAZINGLY, THE LIZARD CHANGES COLOR TO BLEND IN WITH HIS SURROUNDINGS.

MOMENTS LATER, HE IS VIRTUALLY INVISIBLE.

I SEE YOU HIDING BACK THERE! NOW COME CLEAN UP THIS MESS YOU MADE IN THE KITCHEN!

HOLD STILL. THERE'S A MONSTER HORSEFLY ON YOUR HEAD.

POW!!

CAN YOU BELIEVE IT? I MISSED!

!

SO EXCUSE *ME* FOR TRYING TO HELP! YOU WANNA SCRATCH A STINGING WELT ALL DAY? *FINE!* GO AWAY!

NO, WAIT. THERE'S A MOSQUITO ON YOU.

HEY HOBBES, WANT TO SEE AN ANTELOPE?

AN ANTELOPE?!

C'MON!

SEE, SHE'S COMING DOWN THE LADDER TO HER BOYFRIEND'S CAR!

YOU'RE NOT LAUGHING.

IT'S NOT FUNNY.

TOMORROW IS INDEPENDENCE DAY.

THE DECLARATION OF INDEPENDENCE SAYS EVERYONE IS CREATED EQUAL AND IS ENTITLED TO LIFE, LIBERTY AND THE PURSUIT OF HAPPINESS.

OH.

SO WHEN DOES PAUL REVERE RIDE THROUGH TOWN AND GIVE US OUR PRESENTS?

BANG!

KAPWINNGG!

UP, UP AND AWAAAYY!

**CALVIN and HOBBES** by WATTERSON

THE DREADED SCUM BEINGS FIRE! SPACEMAN SPIFF IS *HIT!*

IT NEVER FAILS. I JUST WASHED AND WAXED THIS THING.

OUR HERO, THE INTREPID SPACEMAN SPIFF, STRUGGLES WITH THE CONTROLS OF HIS DAMAGED SPACECRAFT!

THE FREEM PROPULSION BLASTERS ARE USELESS! SPIFF CRASHES ONTO THE SURFACE OF AN ALIEN PLANET!

UNSCATHED, THE FEARLESS SPACE EXPLORER EMERGES FROM THE SMOLDERING WRECKAGE! HE IS MAROONED ON A HOSTILE WORLD!

SCORCHED BY TWIN SUNS, THE PLANET IS NOTHING BUT BARREN ROCK AND METHANE! THERE'S NO HOPE OF FINDING FOOD OR WATER!

SPIFF COLLAPSES! OH NO, A HIDEOUS ALIEN SPOTS HIM! IN HIS WEAKENED STATE, SPIFF IS NO MATCH FOR THE MONSTER! *THIS COULD BE THE END!!*

LUNCHTIME! I BROUGHT YOU A SANDWICH AND SOME LEMONADE.

BRING THE DISHES BACK WHEN YOU'RE DONE, OK?

...OH WELL.

THANKS, MOM.

QUICK, MOM! ALIENS JUST LANDED IN THE BACK YARD! THEY DEMAND TO TALK TO YOU!

YOU GO ON OUT! I'LL GUARD THE COOKIES IN THE KITCHEN!

QUICK! HURRY!

SHE'S NOT BUYING THIS.

CALVIN, JUST HOW DUMB DO YOU THINK I AM?

WHAT DO YOU THINK IS THE SECRET TO HAPPINESS? IS IT MONEY, POWER OR FAME?

I'D CHOOSE MONEY. IF YOU HAVE ENOUGH MONEY, YOU CAN BUY POWER AND FAME. THAT WAY YOU'D HAVE IT ALL AND BE REALLY HAPPY!

HAPPINESS IS BEING FAMOUS FOR YOUR FINANCIAL ABILITY TO INDULGE IN EVERY KIND OF EXCESS.

I SUPPOSE THAT'S ONE WAY TO DEFINE IT.

THE PART I THINK I'D LIKE BEST IS CRUSHING PEOPLE WHO GET IN MY WAY.

LOOK! SOMEBODY POURED NEW CEMENT!

IS ANYONE LOOKING? WE COULD WRITE OUR INITIALS IN IT, OR MAKE A HAND PRINT, OR SOMETHING!

YEAH! "OR SOMETHING"!

I THINK WE'D BETTER FIND A HOSE QUICK!

I DIDN'T THINK IT WOULD SET UP SO FAST.

# Calvin and Hobbes
by WATTERSON

CAN YOU BELIEVE THIS? SOME IDIOT TOSSED GARBAGE HERE IN THIS BEAUTIFUL SPOT.

I'LL BET FUTURE CIVILIZATIONS FIND OUT MORE ABOUT US THAN WE'D LIKE THEM TO KNOW.

LOOK, ANOTHER CAN THROWN ON THE GROUND! BOY, THIS MAKES ME MAD!

BY GOLLY, IF PEOPLE AREN'T BURYING TOXIC WASTES OR TESTING NUCLEAR WEAPONS, THEY'RE THROWING TRASH EVERYWHERE!

YOU'D THINK PLANETS LIKE THIS WERE A DIME A DOZEN! NOW I'VE GOT TO CARRY THIS GROSS THING.

YOU KNOW, THERE ARE TIMES WHEN IT'S A SOURCE OF PERSONAL PRIDE TO NOT BE HUMAN.

I'M WITH YOU.

ARENT THESE LONG SUMMER DAYS GREAT? NO RESPONSIBILITIES AT ALL! WE HAVE THE WHOLE DAY TO OURSELVES.

DON'T YOU WISH IT COULD BE LIKE THIS ALL YEAR, FOREVER? NO SCHOOL, NO JOB, NO ANYTHING?

YEAH, JUST GLOAT ABOUT IT, WHY DON'T YOU!!

HEY DAD, WHAT ARE CLOUDS MADE OF?

HMM... I USED TO KNOW THAT. I THINK THEY'RE MOSTLY WATER.

SO HOW COME THEY FLOAT?

WELL, IT'S SORT OF EVAPORATED WATER. MAYBE THERE ARE SOME OTHER GASES, TOO. I'M NOT SURE.

SO WHY ARE THEY WHITE WHEN THE REST OF THE SKY IS BLUE?

HECK, BEATS ME. I GUESS WE OUGHT TO LOOK THIS STUFF UP.

I TAKE IT THERE'S NO QUALIFYING EXAM TO BE A DAD.

ONE OF THE BEST THINGS ABOUT SUMMER IS GOING TO SLEEP WITH THE FAN ON.

THE GENTLE BREEZE BLOWING, THE DRONING HUM...EVERYTHING SEEMS SAFE AND SERENE WHEN THE FAN IS ON.

IT'S COOL AND LULLING AND PERFECT FOR SLEEP.

IT ALMOST LETS ONE FORGET HE HAS A HEAVY FUR COAT FOR A BUNKMATE.

IF YOU DON'T LIKE IT, THERE'S PLENTY OF ROOM ON THE FLOOR, BUSTER.

40

**Calvin and Hobbes** by WATTERSON

TIGERS ARE NATURAL-BORN TREE CLIMBERS.

THAT'S IT, YOU CLIMB UP AND THEN HELP ME UP!

OF COURSE, WE USUALLY HAVE GRAPPLING HOOKS, ROPES AND UTILITY BELTS.

HEY, HERE'S A GREAT TREE FOR CLIMBING! LET ME GET ON YOUR SHOULDERS SO I CAN REACH THE FIRST BRANCH, OK?

GEEZ, HOW MANY BRICKS DO YOU HAVE IN YOUR POCKETS?!

WHOA! HOLD STEADY, YOU WEAKLING!

I'VE ALMOST GOT IT! MOVE UP, MOVE UP!

HURRY AND GRAB IT BEFORE MY SPINE TELESCOPES.

GOT IT! ...HEY, DON'T LET GO! HOLD ME UP!

FORGET IT! YOU CAN SUPPORT YOUR OWN WEIGHT, BOWLING BALL BUTT.

MMPH! MMPH! I CAN'T GET UP! GIVE ME A BOOST!

HEY! WHAT ARE YOU DOING?! DON'T TAKE OFF MY SHOES!

ARE YOU NUTS? HEY, STOP!

AACK! OH NO! DON'T TICKLE! PBTH! EEK! HEE HEE HA HA! STOP IT! I CAN'T HOLD ON!

HEE HEE HOO HOO

AAUGH!

NICE LANDING. I'M PROBABLY PARALYZED.

ALL EXCEPT YOUR MOUTH, OBVIOUSLY. I'M NOT SORRY AT ALL. GIVE ME BACK MY SHOES.

NO.

DEEP IN A DANK DUNGEON ON THE DISMAL PLANET ZOG, THE FEARLESS SPACEMAN SPIFF IS HELD PRISONER BY THE SINISTER ZOG KING.

A GUARD LEADS SPIFF TO THE INTERROGATION ROOM. OUR HERO IS STOIC AND DEFIANT!

AT LAST I MEET THE FAMED SPACEMAN SPIFF! I TRUST YOU ARE...HEH HEH... ENJOYING YOUR VISIT?

YOU'RE WASTING YOUR TIME, MAGGOT FROM MARS! I'LL NEVER GIVE IN!

NEVER, YOU HEAR ME?! *NEVER!*

KID, DON'T MAKE ME RECANT THE HIPPOCRATIC OATH, OK?

WELL, YOU CERTAINLY WERE A TERROR IN THE DOCTOR'S OFFICE.

I FENDED HIM OFF WITH HIS OWN TONGUE DEPRESSOR. THAT'S WHY I DIDN'T GET A SHOT.

YOU DIDN'T *NEED* A SHOT. YOUR BEHAVIOR WAS INEXCUSABLE.

ALL THAT COUNTS IS THAT HE COULDN'T GET NEAR ENOUGH TO STICK ME. HE THINKS I'M A LITTLE PINK PIN CUSHION IN UNDERPANTS.

SOMEDAY I HOPE YOU HAVE A KID THAT PUTS YOU THROUGH WHAT I'VE GONE THROUGH.

YEAH, GRANDMA SAYS THAT'S WHAT SHE USED TO TELL *YOU.*

HERE IS A PROUD CITY, FULL OF HAPPY, PROSPEROUS CITIZENS.

THEY GO ON ABOUT THEIR BUSINESS, **UNAWARE** THAT THE MOON HAS MYSTERIOUSLY MOVED A FEW MILES CLOSER TO THE EARTH.

...UNAWARE, THAT IS, UNTIL THE TIDE COMES IN.

SPLOOSH!

*GISSHHH!*

# Calvin and Hobbes
## by WATTERSON

THE FIRE'S NOT LIGHTING, HUH? CAN I MAKE A SUGGESTION?

GIVE UP ON THAT SISSY LIGHTER FLUID.

CAN'T WE COOK THE HAMBURGERS YET?

THE COALS AREN'T HOT ENOUGH.

BUT I'M HUNGRY! I WANT TO EAT *NOW!*

WELL, YOU'LL JUST HAVE TO WAIT.

YOU KNOW, CALVIN, SOMETIMES THE ANTICIPATION OF SOMETHING IS MORE FUN THAN THE THING ITSELF ONCE YOU GET IT.

HERE WE ARE, IT'S A BEAUTIFUL EVENING. IT'S NICE TO JUST SIT HERE AND LOOK AT THE TREES WHILE WE WAIT FOR THE COALS TO GET HOT, DON'T YOU THINK?

DINNER WILL BE OVER SOON, AND AFTERWARD WE'LL BE DISTRACTED WITH OTHER THINGS TO DO. BUT NOW WE HAVE A FEW MINUTES TO OURSELVES TO ENJOY THE EVENING.

THESE SUMMER DAYS GO BY SO QUICKLY. IT'S GOOD THAT EVERY NOW AND THEN WE HAVE TO WAIT FOR SOMETHING.

SO SHOULD I GO TO McDONALD'S THEN, OR WHAT?

YEAH, I KNOW. YOU THINK YOU'RE GOING TO BE SIX ALL YOUR LIFE.

45

# Calvin and Hobbes

by WATTERSON

WIPE THAT GRIN OFF YOUR FACE!

WELL, HOBBES, HOW DO I LOOK?

I'M DOING MY BEST TO BITE MY TONGUE.

I CUT OUT CONSTRUCTION PAPER FEATHERS AND TAPED THEM ON MY ARMS SO I CAN FLY! PRETTY NEAT, HUH?

IF PAPER FEATHERS ARE ALL IT TAKES TO FLY, DON'T YOU THINK WE'D HAVE HEARD ABOUT IT BEFORE?

IT TAKES AN UNCOMMON MIND TO THINK OF THESE THINGS, HOBBES.

I'D AGREE WITH THAT.

HERE'S A GORGE. THIS IS A GOOD SPOT.

YOU'RE GOING TO JUMP OFF THIS LEDGE?

HECK NO! I NEED *MOMENTUM!* I WANT YOU TO *TOSS* ME OVER.

YOU UNDERSTAND I ASSUME NO RESPONSIBILITY FOR THIS?

RIGHT. *I* GET THE PATENT.

HEAVE!

I'M FLYING! I'M FLYING!

I'M..... UH OH...

DON'T SELL THE BIKE SHOP, ORVILLE.

SHUT UP AND GO GET ME SOME ANTISEPTIC.

WATTERSON

# Calvin and Hobbes

by WATTERSON

THAT RUN DOESN'T COUNT! YOU DIDN'T TOUCH THIRD BASE!

THAT'S 'CAUSE THIRD BASE CRAWLED TO THE OUTFIELD!

WAP!

HA HA! EASY OUT!!

HEY! WHERE ARE YOU GOING?!

YOU HAVE TO STAY ON THE BASE LINE, YOU CHEATER!

YEAH? PROVE IT!

THIS ISN'T FAIR! YOU CAN'T RUN ANYWHERE!

JUST WATCH ME!

IF WE HAD A FIRST BASEMAN, YOU'D'VE BEEN OUT LONG AGO!

BUT WE DON'T, DO WE?

GOTCHA! YOU'RE OUT!

OK, I'M UP TO BAT AGAIN! WHAT FUN! TWO-MAN BASEBALL IS A *REAL* SPORT!

A REAL SPORT FOR IDIOTS. NEXT TIME I'M GOING TO TAG YOU OUT WITH THE BAT INSTEAD OF THE BALL.

WHEN'S THIS RAIN GOING TO LET UP?

I DON'T KNOW, CALVIN.

HEY, CHEER UP, GANG! I PACKED STORM GEAR. "ALWAYS BE PREPARED," YOU KNOW.

THESE PONCHOS ARE SUPER. THEY'RE THERMAL-SEALED LIGHTWEIGHT NYLON, LAMINATED WITH FLEXIBLE URETHANE FOR COMPLETE WATER PROTECTION!

YEAH, DAD. IT'S GREAT THAT WE WON'T GET WETTER THAN WE ALREADY ARE.

ZINC OXIDE, THONGS, TANNING LOTION... WRONG DUFFEL BAG. LET'S SEE, WHICH ONE OF THESE WAS IT?

I'M GLAD DAD FINALLY GOT THE TENTS UP. NOW I CAN GET OUT OF THESE SOGGY CLOTHES.

TOO BAD *YOU* CAN'T PUT ON DRY CLOTHES. YOU'D FEEL A LOT BETTER.

HEY, WAIT! **NO! DON'T DO THAT HERE!!**

ACKPTH!

SOME TROUPER *YOU* ARE! WHAT'S A LITTLE RAIN? THIS IS WHAT BEING IN THE WILDERNESS IS ALL ABOUT!

HA HA! AT LEAST IT'S NOT *SNOWING*, RIGHT?

RIGHT?

I MEAN, SAY IT WAS SNOWING SO HARD WE COULDN'T MAKE A FIRE.

BOY, I LOVE COLD CANNED RAVIOLI.

WELL, GANG, I'M SORRY THE WEATHER WASN'T ANY BETTER THIS WEEK.

I KNOW IT WASN'T ALWAYS A LOT OF FUN, BUT WE LIVED THROUGH IT, AND WE GOT TO SPEND SOME TIME TOGETHER, AND THAT'S WHAT'S REALLY IMPORTANT.

ANYWAY, I HOPE YOU'RE ALL NOT **TOO** DISAPPOINTED.

CALVIN, TELL YOUR DAD ANY JUDGE WOULD TAKE THIS TRIP AS GROUNDS FOR DIVORCE.

DAD, MOM SAYS...

ALL RIGHT! ALL RIGHT!

---

DAD, CAN YOU GET MY BALL OUT OF THE GUTTER AGAIN?

THIS IS THE THIRD TIME THIS AFTERNOON! I THOUGHT I TOLD YOU TO PLAY OUT BACK!

RELAX, DAD. IT'S JUST A BALL IN THE GUTTER. IT'S NOT AS IF I'VE BEEN EMBEZZLING MONEY OR KILLING PEOPLE, RIGHT? AREN'T YOU GLAD I'M NOT STEALING AND MURDERING?

I ALWAYS HAVE TO HELP DAD ESTABLISH THE PROPER CONTEXT.

---

C'MON, HOBBES. LET DOWN THE ROPE LADDER.

WHAT'S THE REST OF THE PASSWORD?

I THINK FIVE VERSES EXTOLLING TIGERS IS **PLENTY**. YOU KNOW IT'S ME! LET ME UP!

NO.

OOH, WHY YOU LOUSY, ROTTEN, STINKING..

IF YOU CALL ME NAMES, YOU HAVE TO START OVER AT THE BEGINNING.

VERSE SIX: "TIGERS ARE NIMBLE AND LIGHT ON THEIR TOES, MY **RE**SPECT FOR TIGERS CONTINUALLY GROWS."

YOU'RE NOT DOING THE DANCE.

# Calvin and Hobbes by WATTERSON

AH·CHOO!

*WHEW* ...NO BRAINS.

AH.. AH.. AH.. AH

CHOOO!!

THE FORCE OF THE NASAL EXPLOSION SENDS CALVIN REELING THROUGH THE STRATOSPHERE!

WITH LESS AND LESS AIR TO RESIST HIS MOMENTUM, HE BREAKS THE PULL OF EARTH'S GRAVITY AND HURLS PAST THE MOON!

AS HE PASSES OUT OF THE GALAXY, CALVIN REFLECTS ON THE WISDOM OF COVERING ONE'S MOUTH WHEN SNEEZING TO DEFLECT THE PROPULSION.

ALAS, IT IS KNOWLEDGE GAINED TOO LATE FOR POOR CALVIN, THE HUMAN SATELLITE! ...BUT WAIT! ANOTHER SNEEZE IS BREWING! CALVIN TURNS HIMSELF AROUND!

THE SECOND SNEEZE ROCKETS HIM BACK TO EARTH! HE'S SAVED! IT'S A MIRACLE!

AH CHOO!

GOD BLESS YOU.

OH, HE *DOES*, MOM, HE *DOES*.

WATTERSON

THE END OF SUMMER IS ALWAYS HARD ON ME.

...TRYING TO CRAM IN ALL THE GOOFING OFF I'VE BEEN MEANING TO DO.

HOW COME YOU'RE STILL HOME? WHY AREN'T YOU AT WORK?

I TOOK THE DAY OFF.

SAY, DAD, CAN I HAVE A LOOK AT THE CLASSIFIED SECTION?

AS SOON AS I'M THROUGH WITH IT.

GOSH, DAD, I'D SURE LIKE TO BORROW THAT SECTION RIGHT THIS MINUTE. WHY DON'T YOU READ THE EDITORIALS?

"NEW DAD WANTED. FREQUENT TRAVELER PREFERRED. LIBERAL VIEWS ON DISCIPLINE A MUST. ASK FOR CALVIN DURING NORMAL WORK HOURS."

I DON'T *WANNA* TAKE A BATH! I *HATE* TAKING BATHS!

AAAAAAAAAAAAAAAA

NO NO NO NO NO NO NO NO NO NO NO NO NO NO

THEY CAN MAKE ME DO IT, BUT THEY CAN'T MAKE ME DO IT WITH DIGNITY.

RATS. I CAN'T TELL MY GUM FROM MY SILLY PUTTY.

WAP WAP WAP WAP

WIPPITY WAPPITY WIPPITY WAPPITY

BIPPITA BIPPITA BIPPITA BIPPITA BIPPITA

I'M NEVER GONNA GET MARRIED. ARE YOU?

HMM... I SUPPOSE IF THE RIGHT PERSON CAME ALONG, I MIGHT.

SOMEBODY WITH GREEN EYES AND A NICE LAUGH, WHO I COULD CALL "POOTY PIE."

"POOTY PIE"?!?

OR "BITSY POOKUMS."

I THINK THAT WOULD AFFECT MY STOMACH A LOT MORE THAN MY HEART.

"BITSY POOKUMS," I'D SAY. "YES, SNOOGY WOOGY," SHE'D REPLY...

# calvin and hobbes
### by WATTERSON

STIR STIR

STRETTCCHHH

STAB STAB

PAT PAT PAT

MUSH MUSH

SNIFF

HWOOF!

LICK

ACKPTGH

BLECHH

GLUG GLUG GLUG

SMACK

BR-R-R-R

HAAAKK HOCCHH

CHOKE... GASP...

THERE...(PANT)... SEE?
I...I... *TRIED* IT. (COUGH)
IT... ALMOST (WHEEZE)
KILLED... ME.

CLAP CLAP CLAP CLAP CL

ENCORE.  BRA*VO*.

I'M GOING TO RUN AWAY TO ALASKA.

WE MADE IT! IT'S A GOOD THING THE TIME MACHINE DIDN'T STALL, OR WE'D HAVE BEEN EATEN BY DINOSAURS!

WE'RE COMING BACK TOWARD THE PRESENT NOW. DO YOU WANT TO STOP AT HOME, OR KEEP GOING INTO THE FUTURE LIKE WE PLANNED?

I'VE HAD ENOUGH TIME TRAVELING. LET'S GO HOME.

LET'S GO JUST A *LITTLE* INTO THE FUTURE AND SEE WHAT I'M LIKE AS A TEEN-AGER!

LET'S NOT, ALL RIGHT?

HI, MOM. HOBBES AND I WENT TIME TRAVELING AND VISITED THE JURASSIC PERIOD TODAY.

THAT'S NICE. WHAT'S IT LIKE?

PRETTY SCARY. A DINOSAUR ALMOST ATE US.

ACTUALLY, WE WERE TRYING TO GO INTO THE FUTURE, BUT WE MADE A MISTAKE.

I SEE. WELL, I'M GLAD YOU MADE IT BACK.

YOUR MOM ISN'T FAZED BY MUCH, IS SHE?

IT DEPENDS. SHE DIDN'T TAKE THE FROGS IN THE TOILET SO WELL, REMEMBER?

DAD, LOOK! THE SUN'S SETTING AND IT'S ONLY 3 O'CLOCK!

IT'S NOT 3 O'CLOCK. YOUR WATCH STOPPED.

TIME DOESN'T STOP IF YOUR WATCH STOPS?

NOPE.

PHOOEY. FOR A MOMENT THERE, I THOUGHT I'D GET RICH PATENTING THIS THING.

*I'D* HAVE BOUGHT ONE.

IF YOU COULD HAVE THREE WISHES GRANTED, WHAT WOULD THEY BE?

JUST THREE WISHES, HUH? HMM... THAT WOULD BE A TOUGH DECISION.

I GUESS I'D HAVE TO THINK ABOUT IT A WHILE.

OOPS! HANG ON.

OK, I KNOW WHAT MY FIRST WISH WOULD BE.

ONE OF NATURE'S UGLIER CREATURES, THE BAT IS A MISUNDERSTOOD MARVEL OF EVOLUTION.

PRODUCING A SERIES OF LOUD, HIGH-PITCHED SQUEAKS, THE BAT CAN JUDGE AN INSECT'S DISTANCE AND ELEVATION BY THE TIME DELAY OF THE SQUEAK'S ECHO!

CHANGES IN THE ECHO'S PITCH REVEAL THE DOOMED BUG'S DIRECTION! NO MOVEMENT ESCAPES THE INCREDIBLE SENSES OF THE BAT!

GLUMP!

TA-DAA! EYES CLOSED!

CALVIN, SIT UP AND EAT WITH A FORK LIKE A CIVILIZED HUMAN BEING.

YAWN

WAAUUGHH!

FOR THE LAST TIME, GET OUT OF BED! WE'RE GOING TO BE LATE.

I'M TRYING. I'M TRYING.

MOM WANTS ME TO CLEAN MY ROOM. THIS IS THE LAST STRAW!

I DON'T HAVE TO PUT UP WITH THIS TOTALITARIANISM! I'M SECEDING!

GEE, CAN YOU SECEDE FROM YOUR OWN FAMILY?

WHY NOT?! I NEVER SIGNED UP FOR THIS GROUP! I WASN'T EVEN CONSULTED!

THE ONLY REASON MOM AND DAD ARE MY PARENTS IS BECAUSE I WAS *BORN* TO THEM!

A BIOLOGICAL CONSPIRACY, HUH?

WE CAN LIVE ANYWHERE WE WANT TO NOW THAT WE'RE SECEDING FROM THE FAMILY!

WHERE DO YOU WANT TO GO? THE SAHARA? ANTARCTICA?

HOW ARE WE GOING TO GET TO ANY OF *THOSE* PLACES? WE DON'T EVEN HAVE A CAR!

OK DAD, FOR *THIS* AMAZING TRICK I'LL NEED AN ORDINARY AMERICAN EXPRESS CARD. NOW CLOSE YOUR EYES...

HOBBES AND I ARE SECEDING FROM THIS FAMILY, MOM.

OH REALLY?

YEP. WE'RE TAKING MY SLED AND MOVING TO THE YUKON.

WELL, *THAT'S* A LONG WAY AWAY.

I KNOW. HERE'S A LIST OF SANDWICHES AND SUPPLIES WE'LL NEED.

WHY SHOULD I DO ALL THIS IF YOU'RE SECEDING FROM THE FAMILY?

WE HAVEN'T SECEDED *YET!* GEEZ, WHAT KIND OF MOM *ARE* YOU?

HI, CALVIN. I BROUGHT MR. BUN OVER SO WE CAN PLAY HOUSE. YOU AND I CAN BE THE PARENTS, AND HOBBES AND MR. BUN CAN BE OUR CHILDREN.

OH, RIGHT. HOBBES AND I ARE GONNA PUT OUR BIG PLANS ON HOLD SO WE CAN PLAY HOUSE WITH A STUFFED RABBIT? FORGET IT!

I DON'T SEE WHY YOU'LL PLAY WITH YOUR DUMB OL' TIGER AND NOT WITH MR. BUN AND ME! YOU'RE JUST MEAN, THAT'S ALL!

GO PLAY IN A MICROWAVE, SUSIE. WE'RE BUSY.

GIRLS ARE LIKE SLUGS— THEY PROBABLY SERVE SOME PURPOSE, BUT IT'S HARD TO IMAGINE WHAT.

MR. BUN SEEMS COMATOSE. DID YOU NOTICE?

HI, DAD. I'M REPEATING EVERYTHING ANYONE SAYS.

OH, YOU ARE, ARE YOU?

OH, YOU ARE, ARE YOU?

KNOCK IT OFF, CALVIN. THAT'S VERY ANNOYING.

KNOCK IT OFF, CALVIN. THAT'S VERY ANNOYING.

I FORFEIT ALL MY DESSERTS FOR A WEEK.

OK, GIVE THEM TO ME.

HA HA. WHY DON'T YOU GO BOTHER YOUR MOTHER FOR A WHILE?

WHERE ARE YOU GOING WITH THE TOY TELEPHONE?

OUT IN THE WOODS. YOU CAN COME ALONG IF YOU'D LIKE.

WHAT ARE YOU GOING TO DO?

TRY SOME BIRD CALLS.

# CALViN and HobbES

by WATTERSON

HA HA! RIGHT HERE, KID!

EEP!

HELP! HELP! THE LEAF PILE'S GOT ME!!

CRUNCH CRUNCH

WATTERSON

THE RAKE! GOTTA GET THE RAKE!

FORGET IT, KID! YOU'RE DOOMED!

YAAHH! BACK, YOU ARBOREAL MENACE! BACK!

WHAM WHAM

SINISTER FIEND! YOU WON'T BE TRICKING *OTHER* INNOCENT LITTLE KIDS! I'LL SPREAD YOU ACROSS THE WHOLE YARD!

I THOUGHT YOU SAID YOU WERE GOING TO RAKE THE YARD TODAY.

I *DID* RAKE THE YARD. I SPENT ALL AFTERNOO— WHERE'S CALVIN?!

YOUR DAD AND I ARE GOING OUT TO SEE A MOVIE TONIGHT.

CAN I COME TOO?

NO, YOU'RE STAYING HOME.

WHAT, I GOT THE PLAGUE?! WHY CAN'T I COME?

BECAUSE OTHER PEOPLE LIKE TO WATCH MOVIES WITHOUT HEARING ADVICE SHOUTED TO THE CHARACTERS ON THE SCREEN.

SO WHO DOES *THAT*? ARE YOU SAYING *I* DO THAT?

MOM WON'T LET US GO TO THE MOVIE WITH THEM, SO I GUESS WE'RE ON OUR OWN TONIGHT.

CAN WE WATCH TV?

WHAT MOM AND DAD DON'T KNOW WON'T HURT 'EM, RIGHT?

IN FACT, AFTER THEY LEAVE, LET'S GET IN THE OTHER CAR AND LEARN TO DRIVE!

OH BOY! I GET TO BEEP THE HORN, OK?

HEY, THERE'S A TEEN-AGER COMING UP THE DRIVE. OH NO! IT'S *ROSALYN*!

**OUR BABY SITTER?!** WHAT'S SHE DOING HERE? DON'T MOM AND DAD *TRUST* US?? QUICK, HIDE!!

WE'RE LEAVING NOW, ROSALYN. CALVIN IS UPSTAIRS.

I HOPE HE'S NOT TOO MUCH TROUBLE TONIGHT.

DON'T WORRY, I BROUGHT A CATTLE PROD THIS TIME!

YOUR MOM AND DAD LAUGHED. MAYBE IT WAS A JOKE.

MAYBE MOM AND DAD THINK SCORCHING LITTLE KIDS IS FUNNY. LET'S GO.

# Calvin and Hobbes by WATTERSON

**POW!!**

PANT WHEEZE GASP

WELL, IF YOU DIDN'T GET IN A FIGHT AT SCHOOL, WHAT ON EARTH HAPPENED TO YOU?!

LET'S JUST SAY SOMETIMES I WISH I HAD A GERBIL.

75

UH OH, IT HAPPENED AGAIN.

CALVIN WAKES UP WITHOUT ANY RECOGNIZABLE FEATURES, SAVE TWO ANTENNAE. HOW DISGUSTING.

HE OOZES OUT OF BED ON A TRAIL OF SLIME. LACKING ARMS AND LEGS, HOW WILL CALVIN PUT ON HIS CLOTHES?

AREN'T YOU DRESSED YET? YOU ARE SO SLUGGISH IN THE MORNING!

PSST...SUSIE! WHAT'S THE ANSWER TO QUESTION FOUR?

IMADOOFUS.

THANKS!

THE TOOTH FAIRY'S GONNA MAKE YOU RICH TONIGHT, SUSIE.

LET'S SEE WHAT YOU DREW FOR ART CLASS, SUSIE.

WELL, A TIDY LITTLE DOMESTIC SCENE. A HOUSE IN A YARD WITH FLOWERS. HOW TYPICALLY FEMALE.

GIRLS THINK SMALL AND ARE PREOCCUPIED WITH PETTY DETAILS. BUT *BOYS* THINK *BIG!* BOYS THINK ABOUT ACTION AND ACCOMPLISHMENT! NO WONDER IT'S *MEN* WHO CHANGE THE WORLD!

YEAH? WHAT DID *YOU* DRAW?

A SQUADRON OF B-1s NUKING NEW YORK.

**SHOVE**

PEOPLE WHO GET NOSTALGIC ABOUT CHILDHOOD WERE OBVIOUSLY NEVER CHILDREN.

**Panel 1:** PROCESSED LUNCH MEAT IS PRETTY SCARY. WHAT *ARE* THESE LITTLE SPECKS, ANYWAY? LIZARD PARTS? WHO KNOWS?

**Panel 2:** AND THIS "SKIN"! I HEARD IT USED TO BE MADE OF INTESTINE, BUT I THINK NOWADAYS IT'S PLASTIC.

**Panel 3:** OF COURSE, THEY DYE AND WAX FRUIT SO IT LOOKS BETTER. IT'S LIKE EATING A CANDLE.

**Panel 4:** AND MOM WONDERS WHY I'M SO HUNGRY AFTER SCHOOL.

YEP, WE'D PROBABLY BE DEAD NOW IF IT WASN'T FOR TWINKIES.

**Panel 5:** HEY, DAD, YOUR LATEST POLL JUST CAME IN. LET'S SEE WHAT IT SAYS.

BE STILL, MY HEART.

**Panel 6:** WELL, I'LL BE! YOUR POPULARITY IS IMPROVING! YOU WENT UP 30 POINTS!

REALLY?

**Panel 7:** HECK, NO WONDER! I'M READING THE GRAPH UPSIDE-DOWN. WHAT A KLUTZ I AM!

**Panel 8:** ...HOPE YOU'RE ALL PACKED, DAD.

DON'T YOU HAVE SOME HOMEWORK TO DO?

SNIFF SNIFF

**Panel 12:** I LIKE TO MESS WITH HIS DREAMS.

ZZ...COOKIES? FOR ME? WHY SURE, BACK UP THE TRUCK... ZZZZ

THINK IT'S GETTING ANY COLDER OUT?

NOT REALLY.

I DON'T THINK IT'S GONNA CHANGE.

ME EITHER.

NUTS. WELL, LET'S GO IN.

WHATCHA DOIN'?

COUNTERFEITING MONEY.

IT'S REALLY HARD. LOOK AT ALL THE LITTLE LINES ON THIS BILL.

THINK ANYONE WILL FALL FOR YOUR FORGERY?

SURE. EVERYONE WILL.

OL' GEORGE HAS THE GOUT, I SEE.

I *SAID* THIS WAS HARD.

THE GIANT WHALE SWIMS TOWARD THE SURFACE!

ITS MASSIVE TAIL PUMPING FURIOUSLY, HE GAINS TERRIFYING MOMENTUM!

THE 35-TON BEHEMOTH BREACHES! HE CRASHES INTO THE SURF WITH DEAFENING IMPACT!

CALVIN, YOU'D BETTER NOT BE SPLASHING THE FLOOR, YOU HEAR ME?!

YAAAAH!

STIR
STIR
STIR

STIR
STIR
STIR

I WON'T EAT ANY CEREAL THAT DOESN'T TURN THE MILK PURPLE.

THE DEADLY TORNADO MAKES ITS WAY ACROSS THE COMMUNITY!

THE CIRCLING UPDRAFT CLOCKS AT OVER 200 MPH! THE TWISTER SEARCHES FOR A TRAILER PARK!

FINDING ONE, IT TOUCHES DOWN! DEBRIS IS THROWN FOR MILES IN THE ENSUING EXPLOSION OF RUSHING AIR!

WHEN ARE YOU GOING TO CLEAN UP THIS ROOM?! IT LOOKS LIKE A...

TORNADO HIT IT, I KNOW.

OH BOY, IT'S SATURDAY!!

WHAT'S GOING ON? WHY AREN'T THERE ANY CARTOONS ON TV? IT'S JUST A TEST PATTERN.

THE TV GUIDE SAYS THEY DON'T START UNTIL 6:30.

HECK, THAT'S 45 MINUTES FROM NOW! WELL, C'MON, I'LL RACE YOU UP AND DOWN THE STAIRS!

WHY CAN'T HE EVER GET UP LIKE THIS ON SCHOOL DAYS?

GO BREAK HIS LITTLE LEGS, WILL YOU, HONEY?

BANG!

BONK

BAD NEWS ON YOUR CAMPAIGN TO STAY DAD, DAD.

OH?

YEP. THE LATEST POLL OF SIX-YEAR-OLDS IN THIS HOUSEHOLD SHOWS THAT THEY DON'T CARE ABOUT ISSUES THIS YEAR. IT'S CHARACTER THAT COUNTS.

SO WHY IS THAT BAD NEWS?

WHO'S THE BIMBO WITH YOU IN THIS OLD PROM PICTURE?

THAT "BIMBO" IS YOUR MOTHER!

WHO'S A BIMBO?!

PRETTY FUNKY HAIRDO, MOM!

IT'S THE SAD TRUTH, DAD. NOBODY CARES ABOUT YOUR POSITIONS ON FATHERHOOD. WE JUST WANT TO KNOW ABOUT YOUR CHARACTER.

IF YOU'RE GOING TO BE DAD HERE, WE HAVE TO KNOW YOU'VE NEVER DONE OR SAID ANYTHING THAT WOULD REFLECT POORLY ON YOUR JUDGMENT.

I HAVE YOUR COLLEGE YEARBOOK HERE. LET'S FLIP THROUGH IT, SHALL WE?

IS THIS YOU WITH THE KEG AND THE "PARTY NAKED" T-SHIRT?

GIVE ME THAAAT!

GRANDPA SAYS THE COMICS WERE A LOT BETTER YEARS AGO WHEN NEWSPAPERS PRINTED THEM BIGGER.

HE SAYS COMICS NOW ARE JUST A BUNCH OF XEROXED TALKING HEADS BECAUSE THERE'S NO SPACE TO TELL A DECENT STORY OR TO SHOW ANY ACTION.

HE THINKS PEOPLE SHOULD WRITE TO THEIR NEWSPAPERS AND COMPLAIN.

YOUR GRANDPA TAKES THE FUNNIES PRETTY SERIOUSLY.

YEAH, MOM'S LOOKING INTO NURSING HOMES.

DID YOU READ THIS? THIS TV STAR MADE OVER TWENTY MILLION DOLLARS LAST YEAR!

WHAT WOULD *YOU* DO WITH TWENTY MILLION BUCKS?

BEATS ME. I THINK IT'S RIDICULOUS THAT ANYONE MAKES THAT KIND OF MONEY.

OK, SAY YOU ONLY MADE *FIFTEEN* MILLION.

LET'S SAY EIGHTEEN.

HI, MOM.

BUM BA DA BUM BUM

WHAT'S COOKING?

HA HA HA HA HA HA!

WHAT'S WITH *YOU*?

I THOUGHT MY LIFE WOULD SEEM MORE INTERESTING WITH A MUSICAL SCORE AND A LAUGH TRACK.

I MADE UP A JOKE. A MAN'S GOING FOR A WALK, SO HE GETS HIS DOG AND SAYS, "HEEL!"

..AND THE DOG LOOKS UP AND SAYS, "IT TAKES ONE TO KNOW ONE, BUSTER!" HA HA HA HA HA!!

WHAT'S THE MATTER WITH YOU? DON'T YOU *GET* IT?!

AHHH, WHAT DO TIGERS KNOW ABOUT SOPHISTICATED HUMOR, ANYWAY?

HOW DID THE DOG LEARN TO TALK?

QUIT HOGGING THE BED. YOU'RE WAY OVER ON MY SIDE.

TOUGH BEANS, FUZZ FACE.

EVER THINK ABOUT GEYSERS AND WATERFALLS? HUNDREDS OF THOUSANDS OF GALLONS OF WATER! FLOWING, SPILLING, RUSHING, GUSHING, SPLASHING!

HE REALLY FIGHTS MEAN.

SPACEMAN SPIFF FLEES THE DESPICABLE SCUM BEINGS OF PLANET Q-13!

IN A SURPRISE MANEUVER, OUR HERO TURNS TO FACE THE ADVERSARY! HIS HAND TIGHTENS AROUND THE DEATH RAY TRIGGER!

IT DOESN'T RESPOND! SPIFF REACHES FOR THE MERTILIZER BEAM, BUT IT DOESN'T WORK EITHER! NEITHER DO THE PHOSPHO BOMBS OR THE MORDO BLASTERS! NOTHING IS WORKING!!

1812! GETTYSBURG! 16 FLUID OUNCES! I BEFORE E! THOMAS EDISON!

PERHAPS SOMEONE WHO HAS BEEN *PAYING ATTENTION* CAN HELP OUT CALVIN?

Z

YAAHH!

I KEEP FORGETTING THAT FIVE OF HIS SIX ENDS ARE POINTY WHEN HE LIES LIKE THAT.

SINCE SEPTEMBER, IT'S JUST GOTTEN COLDER AND COLDER.

THERE'S LESS DAYLIGHT NOW, I'VE NOTICED, TOO.

OH NO! THIS CAN ONLY MEAN ONE THING!

THE SUN IS GOING OUT! IN A FEW MORE MONTHS EARTH WILL BE A DARK AND LIFELESS BALL OF ICE!

WELL, GEE, NOW I DON'T FEEL SO BAD ABOUT NOT SETTING UP AN IRA LAST YEAR.

DAD SAYS THE SUN ISN'T GOING OUT.

HE SAYS IT'S COLDER BECAUSE OUR HEMISPHERE IS TILTED AWAY FROM THE SUN NOW.

HE SAYS WINTER WILL BE HERE SOON.

ISN'T IT SAD HOW SOME PEOPLE'S GRIP ON THEIR LIVES IS SO PRECARIOUS THAT THEY'LL EMBRACE ANY PREPOSTEROUS DELUSION RATHER THAN FACE AN OCCASIONAL BLEAK TRUTH?

ARE YOU GOING TO LIVE THE LAST FEW MONTHS OF YOUR LIFE ANY DIFFERENTLY, NOW THAT THE SUN IS GOING OUT AND WE'RE ALL DOOMED?

NO, I'VE ALWAYS BELIEVED IN LIVING EACH DAY AS IF IT WAS MY LAST, SO I NEVER HAVE ANY REGRETS.

KIND OF INSPIRING, HUH?

IF YOU WERE SOMEONE ELSE, IT MIGHT BE.

PASS ME THAT ISSUE OF CAPTAIN NAPALM WILL YOU?

MY TEACHER SAID THE SAME THING DAD DID. THE SUN *ISN'T* GOING OUT AFTER ALL!

IT'S JUST GETTING COLDER BECAUSE WINTER'S COMING. DAD WAS RIGHT ALL ALONG!

IMAGINE OL' DAD KNOWING SOMETHING LIKE THAT!

WHAT'S THIS STORY YOU'RE GOING TO READ ME, DAD? IT DOESN'T HAVE ANY ROMANCE IN IT, DOES IT?

UH...

EDIT IT OUT IF IT DOES. I HATE ROMANCE. DOES IT HAVE ANY BORING DESCRIPTION IN IT?

WELL...

SKIP IT IF YOU SEE ANY. I LIKE MY STORIES FAST AND GRIPPING.

IT DOESN'T HAVE A MORAL, DOES IT? I HATE BEING TOLD HOW TO LIVE MY LIFE. SKIP THE MORAL, TOO, OK?

DOES HIS MAJESTY PREFER COLOR PICTURES, OR BLACK AND WHITE?

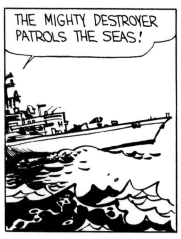

THE MIGHTY DESTROYER PATROLS THE SEAS!

SUDDENLY THE SHIP SPINS OUT OF CONTROL! IT'S CAUGHT IN A WHIRLPOOL!

WITHIN MOMENTS THE GIANT VESSEL DIPS ITS HULL INTO THE SWIRLING VORTEX AND IS NEVER SEEN AGAIN!

OH NO! HERE GOES THE REST OF THE NAVY!

ARE YOU LETTING *THE WATER OUT* ALREADY?

# Calvin and Hobbes

by WATTERSON

CALVIN, IT'S TIME TO WAKE UP.

CALVIN, IT'S TIME TO WAKE UP.

C'MON, YOU'LL BE LATE FOR SCHOOL.

MY DREAMS ARE GETTING WAY TOO LITERAL.

**Panel 1:** I ALWAYS WANTED TO BE A CUB SCOUT AND GET MERIT BADGES AND STUFF, BUT I HATE GOING TO MEETINGS.

OK OK, JUST READ ABOUT KNOTS, ALL RIGHT?

**Panel 2:** HEY, LOOK, HERE'S A MOTTO! I DIDN'T KNOW YOU HAD A MOTTO! WOW, WHAT FUN!

"LIVE FOR REVENGE" IS GOING TO BE MY MOTTO IF YOU DON'T GET ME OUT OF THIS.

WATTERSON

**Panel 3:** I'LL QUIZ YOU. WHAT DO YOU DO FOR A SECOND-DEGREE BURN?

DON'T FLIP THROUGH THE BOOK, YOU IDIOT! UNTIE ME!

**Panel 4:** HMPH, IF I WAS IN YOUR PREDICAMENT, I'D TREAT ME WITH A LOT MORE RESPECT. DO YOU SAY YOU'RE SORRY?

MMFF! RRGGH! OOH! ARGH! YOU DIRTY ROTTEN STINKING

**Panel 5:** HOBBES, I'M NOT KIDDING. IF YOU DON'T GET ME LOOSE IN TEN SECONDS...

YOU GOT YOURSELF INTO THIS, "MR. HOUDINI," NOT ME.

**Panel 6:** BUT I'M SUPPOSED TO BE AT DINNER! MOM'S GONNA KILL ME!

ESCAPE ARTISTS HAVE A RISKY TRADE. HEY, HERE'S MORSE CODE!

**Panel 7:** OK, I'M SORRY I CALLED YOU NAMES. I SAID I'M SORRY, RIGHT? NOW UNTIE ME!

HERE'S HOW YOU SAY "BANANA" IN MORSE. DASH DOT DOT DOT, DOT DASH...

WATTERSON

**Panel 8:** WHAT IS THAT KID *DOING?!* IT SOUNDS LIKE A CHAIR THUMPING AROUND THE ROOM.

WELL, HIS DINNER IS STONE COLD. I HOPE HE'S HAPPY.

BONK BONK

**Panel 9:** ALL RIGHT, YOUNG MAN! YOU'VE WASTED THE NICE MEAL YOUR MOM FIXED. GET OUT HERE.

**Panel 10:** YOU TIED YOURSELF UP?? WHAT ON EARTH WERE YOU *DOING?!*

HOBBES TIED ME UP, DAD! IT'S *HIS* FAULT!

WATTERSON

**Panel 11:** DON'T MAKE UP LIES, CALVIN. HOW DID YOU GET YOURSELF LIKE THIS?!

*HOBBES* DID IT, DAD! HE WAS GOING TO HOLD ME FOR RANSOM! HONEST!

**Panel 12:** RANSOM?? WHO'D PAY FOR *YOU*, YOU BIG FIBBER?! I'M CERTAINLY GLAD YOUR DAD SAW THROUGH *THAT* FILTHY LIE!

OH, HUSH. YOU *ALWAYS* GET ME IN TROUBLE.

# Calvin and Hobbes
by Watterson

First there was nothing...

...then there was Calvin!

Calvin, the mighty god, creates the universe with pure will!

From utter nothingness comes swirling form! Life begins where once was void!

But Calvin is no kind and loving god! He's one of the old gods! He demands sacrifice!

Yes, Calvin is a god of the underworld! And the puny inhabitants of earth displease him!

The great Calvin ignores their pleas for mercy and the doomed writhe in agony!

HAVE YOU SEEN HOW ABSORBED CALVIN IS WITH THOSE TINKERTOYS? HE'S CREATING WHOLE WORLDS OVER THERE!

I'LL BET HE GROWS UP TO BE AN ARCHITECT.

WHAT'S FOR DINNER, MOM?

TORTELLINI.

OH, NO, NOT TORTELLINI! I *HATE* TORTELLINI!! OH, GROSS! YECCH! TORTELLINI!!

NOTHING IS MORE DISGUSTING THAN TORTELLINI!! CAN'T WE HAVE SOMETHING ELSE?

NO.

TORTELLINI... TORTELLINI... T-O-R...

DID YOU SEE WE HAVE A SUBSTITUTE TEACHER TODAY?

OH, NO! THAT CAN ONLY MEAN OUR *REAL* TEACHER ROCKETED BACK TO SATURN TO REPORT TO HER SUPERIORS!

THEY'RE TRYING TO SUBVERT US LITTLE KIDS WITH SUBLIMINAL MESSAGES IN OUR TEXTBOOKS, TELLING US TO TURN IN OUR PARENTS WHEN THE SATURNIANS ATTACK! EARTH WILL BE RENDERED HELPLESS!

I THINK ONE OF US HAS BEEN EATING TOO MUCH PASTE IN ART CLASS.

I'M TOO SMART FOR 'EM, THOUGH! I DON'T READ MY ASSIGNMENTS!

BEHOLD THE TERRIBLE THUNDER LIZARD, TYRANNOSAURUS REX!

THE FIERCEST DINOSAUR OF ALL, HE IS TWENTY TONS OF BONE-CRUSHING MUSCLE AND RAZOR-SHARP TEETH!

ALWAYS THE VICTOR, HE LETS OUT A TRIUMPHANT ROAR!

LIBRARY

BOOT

AH.. **AH..** AH ..

I JUTH *HADE* IT WHED THITH HAPPEDTH.

CALVIN THE CRIMINAL IS ABOUT TO FACE JUSTICE! ANGRY THRONGS TURN OUT TO WATCH HIS EXECUTION!

AS HE IS LED UP THE GALLOWS, HE REFLECTS UPON HIS MANY HEINOUS CRIMES. HE IS NOT REPENTANT!

THE NOOSE IS PUT AROUND HIS NECK AND TIGHTENED! THIS IS THE END!

GACKK URRGHH

OH, KNOCK IT OFF. SOME OF US HAVE TO WEAR A TIE EVERY DAY.

HOW WAS THE KIDDY MATINEE MOVIE?

MOVIE? OH, YEAH, THE MOVIE. YEAH, THERE WAS A MOVIE. IT WAS OK, I GUESS.

HOW WAS THE MATINEE?

WE... ARE... BUYING... A VIDEO PLAYER.

# Calvin and Hobbes

by Watterson

YAWN

PUTT PUTT PUTT PUTT PUTT PUTT

Z

SCRITCH SCRATCH

ZZ
MMM..

RUB RUB RUB

ZZ
..RRRR..

SHOOF SHOOF SHOOF

ZZ
..OOO..MM..

ITCH ITCH ITCH ITCH

ZZ
YOW WOW
YOW WOW
ZZ..

NKG
K
ZZ..

HMMMMM

ZZZ
Z

*THAT* SIGH OUGHT TO GET ME OUT OF A FEW YEARS' PURGATORY.

Z

Dear Santa,

Attached is my Christmas list for this year.

Last year I did not receive several items from my list.

For your convenience, I have grouped those items together on page 12. Please check them carefully, and include them with the rest of my loot this year.

THAT'S THE PROBLEM WITH THIS GUY. HE'S GOTTEN SLOPPY WITHOUT ANY COMPETITION.

HE SEES YOU WHEN YOU'RE SLEEPING, HE KNOWS WHEN YOU'RE AWAKE ...

HE KNOWS IF YOU'VE BEEN BAD OR GOOD, SO BE GOOD FOR GOODNESS SAKE!

* CLICK *

SANTA CLAUS: KINDLY OLD ELF, OR CIA SPOOK?

THIS SANTA CLAUS STUFF BOTHERS ME.... ESPECIALLY THE JUDGE AND JURY BIT.

WHO APPOINTED SANTA? HOW DO WE KNOW HE'S IMPARTIAL? WHAT CRITERIA DOES HE USE FOR DETERMINING GOOD AND BAD?

AND WHAT ABOUT EXTENUATING CIRCUMSTANCES? KIDS SHOULD HAVE THE BENEFIT OF LEGAL COUNSEL, DON'T YOU THINK?

YOU'RE WORRIED ABOUT THE SALAMANDER INCIDENT, AREN'T YOU?

TEMPORARY INSANITY! THAT'S ALL IT WAS!

THEY SAY SANTA KNOWS IF YOU'VE BEEN GOOD OR BAD, BUT WHAT IF SOMEONE HAD BEEN SORT OF *BOTH*?

I MEAN, SUPPOSE SOME KID *TRIED* TO BE GOOD...AT LEAST, WELL, MOST OF THE TIME...BUT BAD THINGS INEXPLICABLY KEPT HAPPENING?

SUPPOSE SOME KID JUST HAD TERRIBLE LUCK, AND HE GOT BLAMED FOR A LOT OF THINGS HE DID ONLY *SORT* OF ON PURPOSE?

WHO EXACTLY MIGHT WE BE TALKING ABOUT?

THIS IS A PURELY HYPOTHETICAL CASE, MR. SMARTY PANTS.

THIS WHOLE SANTA CLAUS THING JUST DOESN'T MAKE SENSE.

WHY ALL THE SECRECY? WHY ALL THE MYSTERY? IF THE GUY EXISTS, WHY DOESN'T HE EVER SHOW HIMSELF AND PROVE IT?

AND IF HE *DOESN'T* EXIST, WHAT'S THE MEANING OF ALL THIS?

I DUNNO... ISN'T THIS A RELIGIOUS HOLIDAY?

YEAH, BUT ACTUALLY, I'VE GOT THE SAME QUESTIONS ABOUT GOD.

GOSH, HOBBES, WHAT IF I DON'T GET ANY PRESENTS THIS YEAR BECAUSE I DOUBTED THE EXISTENCE OF SANTA?

SUPPOSE HE'S PUTTING MY NAME ON THE "BAD" LIST RIGHT NOW! THAT *WOULD* BE AWFUL!

PERSONALLY, I'D THINK THAT IF YOU WEREN'T ON THE "BAD" LIST ALL ALONG, THIS WOULDN'T PUSH YOU OVER.

THANKS FOR THE COMFORT, EGGNOG BRAIN.

SEE? *SEE* WHY YOU'RE ON THE "BAD" LIST? INSULTS!

THIS SNOW FORT CAN REPEL ANY ATTACK!

I HATE THIS NEIGHBORHOOD.

WHAP!

? ? ? ?

I'M GLAD TO SEE *YOU'RE* INSIDE.

IT'S HANDY NOT TO HAVE BOOTS AND A COAT TO TAKE OFF.

MY SNOW FORT MAKES ME INVULNERABLE!

FROM BEHIND ITS THICK WALL, I CAN LAUNCH A BRUTAL SNOWBALL BARRAGE AND REMAIN SAFE FROM RETALIATION!

WHAP!

YOU'RE SUPPOSED TO ATTACK FROM *THAT* SIDE OF THE FORT, DUMMY!!

**Panel 1:** I HATE WAITING FOR THE SCHOOL BUS ON DAYS LIKE THESE.

**Panel 2:** BLUSTERY COLD DAYS SHOULD BE SPENT PROPPED UP IN BED WITH A MUG OF HOT CHOCOLATE AND A PILE OF COMIC BOOKS.

**Panel 3:** THAT'S WHAT I'D LIKE TO BE DOING RIGHT NOW.

**Panel 4:** AS SOON AS I GRADUATE, I'M GOING TO SPEND *EVERY* WINTER THAT WAY.

I WISH YOUR BUS WOULD COME. MY HOT CHOCOLATE WILL GET COLD.

**Panel 5:** HELP ME FIGURE OUT THIS HOMEWORK PROBLEM, HOBBES. WHAT'S 3 + 8?

**Panel 6:** OK, ASSIGN THE ANSWER A VALUE OF "X". "X" ALWAYS MEANS MULTIPLY, SO TAKE THE NUMERATOR (THAT'S LATIN FOR "NUMBER EIGHTER") AND PUT THAT ON THE OTHER SIDE OF THE EQUATION.

**Panel 7:** THAT LEAVES YOU WITH THREE ON THIS SIDE, SO WHAT TIMES THREE EQUALS EIGHT? THE ANSWER, OF COURSE, IS SIX.

**Panel 8:** GOSH, I MUST HAVE DONE ALL THE OTHERS WRONG.

THESE PROBLEMS SEEM AWFULLY ADVANCED FOR FIRST GRADE, IF YOU ASK ME.

**Panel 9:** HERE'S ANOTHER MATH PROBLEM I CAN'T FIGURE OUT. WHAT'S 9 + 4?

**Panel 10:** OOH, THAT'S A TRICKY ONE. YOU HAVE TO USE CALCULUS AND IMAGINARY NUMBERS FOR THIS.

**Panel 11:** IMAGINARY NUMBERS?!

YOU KNOW, ELEVENTEEN, THIRTY-TWELVE, AND ALL THOSE. IT'S A LITTLE CONFUSING AT FIRST.

**Panel 12:** HOW DID *YOU* LEARN ALL THIS? YOU'VE NEVER EVEN GONE TO SCHOOL!

INSTINCT. TIGERS ARE BORN WITH IT.

ITS FREEZING IN THIS HOUSE! SOMEBODY CRANK UP THE THERMOSTAT! WHY DOESN'T SOMEONE MAKE A FIRE?!

IF WE CAN'T AFFORD TO HEAT THIS PLACE, MAYBE DAD SHOULD GET A BETTER JOB! WHY CAN'T WE MOVE TO FLORIDA?!

CALVIN, PIPE DOWN AND PUT ON A SWEATER IF YOU'RE COLD.

AND GO TO ALL THAT TROUBLE?!

---

I READ THAT THE AVERAGE HOUSEHOLD WATCHES 7½ HOURS OF TV EVERY DAY.

MOM SAYS SHE DOESN'T WATCH TV AT ALL WHILE I'M AT SCHOOL...

...SO IF I GET HOME AT 3:00, I SHOULD BE ABLE TO WATCH IT STRAIGHT TILL 10:30, RIGHT?

WRONG. DO YOU WANT US TO BE SUB-AVERAGE?!

---

MOM, THE WASHER IS DONE.

OK.

AREN'T YOU GOING TO PUT THE WASH IN THE DRYER?

IN A MINUTE.

YOU MEAN YOU'RE JUST GOING TO LET IT SIT IN THE WASHING MACHINE?!?

CALVIN, CAN'T YOU SEE I'M BUSY RIGHT NOW??

SHE SAYS SHE'S BUSY.

I HOPE THE NEXT TIME SHE TAKES A BATH THERE AREN'T ANY TOWELS.

# Calvin and Hobbes by Watterson

114

**WHO'S** COMING TO VISIT?

YOUR UNCLE MAX. I THOUGHT I TOLD YOU.

UNCLE MAX?? **I** DON'T REMEMBER ANY UNCLE MAX. ARE YOU SURE HE'S RELATED? MAYBE HE'S A CON MAN TRYING TO SWINDLE US!

OF COURSE HE'S RELATED. HE'S YOUR DAD'S BROTHER. HE JUST HASN'T BEEN HERE FOR A FEW YEARS.

WHY NOT? WAS HE IN JAIL?

NO! GOOD HEAVENS, CALVIN.

NOW, NOW... WITH MAX, THAT'S NOT A BAD GUESS.

WE'RE GETTING NEAR THE AIRPORT, CALVIN. SEE THE JETS?

HOW COME YOU'RE SO QUIET BACK THERE? AREN'T YOU EXCITED TO SEE UNCLE MAX?

...YEAH...

I JUST HOPE NOBODY THINKS I'M GIVING UP **MY** ROOM WHILE HE'S HERE.

IT'S GREAT TO SEE YOU, MAX! IT SEEMS LIKE AGES SINCE YOU'VE BEEN HERE.

I'LL SAY.

I DIDN'T THINK IT HAD BEEN SO LONG, UNTIL I SAW CALVIN. THIS GUY HAS REALLY GROWN.

SO KID, WHAT DO YOU SAY?

I SAY YOU'D BETTER WATCH YOUR STEP, 'CAUSE I'VE GOT A LIVE, MAN-EATING TIGER AT HOME, AND IF I SO MUCH AS WINK, HE'LL RIP YOUR LUNGS OUT.

CUTE KID, BRO.

DO YOU HAVE ANY KIDS, UNCLE MAX?

ME? NOPE, I'M NOT EVEN MARRIED.

OH.

...WHAT DIFFERENCE DOES *THAT* MAKE?

KID WATCHES A LOT OF TV, DOES HE?

BOY, CALVIN TAKES THAT STUFFED TIGER EVERYWHERE HE GOES.

YEAH, THEY'RE INSEPARABLE.

DO YOU WORRY ABOUT THAT? I MEAN, SHOULDN'T HE BE PLAYING WITH REAL FRIENDS?

OH, I THINK HE WILL WHEN HE'S READY. DIDN'T YOU EVER HAVE AN IMAGINARY FRIEND?

SOMETIMES I THINK *ALL* MY FRIENDS HAVE BEEN IMAGINARY.

UNCLE MAX, LOOK! I'LL SHOW YOU A MAGIC DISAPPEARING TRICK!

OK, FIRST I'LL NEED AN ORDINARY TWENTY-DOLLAR BILL.

HOW ABOUT IF I LEND YOU A NICKEL INSTEAD?

NO, IT WORKS MUCH BETTER WITH A TWENTY. ...OR A FIFTY, IF YOU HAVE ONE.

I TAKE IT YOU THINK YOUR OL' UNCLE MAX IS A LOW-WATT BULB.

WHY, DID DAD TELL YOU HOW THIS WORKS?

# CALVIN and HOBBES

by WATTERSON

SEVEN.. EIGHT... NINE... *TEN!*

THAT'S *MY* SQUARE! HA HA! YOU OWE ME MONEY!

..UH...ELEVEN!

*JUST A MINUTE!*

WHAT ARE YOU DOING?? YOU CAN'T JUST TAKE MONEY FROM THE BANK!

YOU'VE GOT HOTELS ON EVERY PIECE OF PROPERTY YOU OWN. I CAN'T AFFORD TO PAY YOU, SO I'M STICKING UP THE BANK. IT'S A ROBBERY!

YOU CAN'T DO THAT!

I'M THE BANKER, RIGHT? AM I GOING TO RISK MY LIFE OVER A FEW THOUSAND DOLLARS?

THE RULES DON'T SAY YOU CAN ROB THE BANK. THAT'S CHEATING.

DO THE RULES SAY YOU *CAN'T* ROB THE BANK? HUH? *DO* THEY? JUST ROLL THE DICE AND ACCEPT THIS AS A TRAGIC TURN OF EVENTS, OK?

OK, IF *THAT'S* HOW WE'RE PLAYING, THEN *I'M* ROBBING *YOU!*

HA! I'LL STEAL YOUR DEEDS TO PARK PLACE AND BOARDWALK!

YEAH? WELL, I'M TAKING ALL THE HOUSES AND HOTELS, AND PUTTING THEM ON BALTIC, WHERE YOU JUST LANDED! YOU OWE ME $250,000!

THAT'S WHAT *YOU* THINK, YOU... YOU...

ISN'T IT CUTE HOW CALVIN PLAYS BOTH SIDES OF MONOPOLY WITH HIS STUFFED TIGER?

I DUNNO... I OVERHEARD HIM USING WORDS HE DIDN'T LEARN IN *THIS* HOUSEHOLD.

WHAT ARE YOU DOING?! YOU'RE DOODLING! YOU'RE SITTING HERE DRAWING MARTIANS WHEN WE'RE SUPPOSED TO BE RESEARCHING!

YOU HAVEN'T DONE **ANYTHING** YET! DON'T YOU CARE?? WHAT'S THE MATTER WITH YOU?!

IT'S NO USE! WE'RE GOING TO FLUNK! I'LL HAVE TO GO TO A SECOND-RATE COLLEGE BECAUSE MY IDIOT PARTNER SPENT THE STUDY PERIOD DRAWING MARTIANS!

WHY ME? WHY ME? WHY ME?

HERE, THIS WILL CHEER YOU UP. THE MARTIAN MOVES WHEN YOU FLIP THE PAGES! WATCH, YOU CAN SEE HIM EAT AN ASTRONAUT!

LOOK, BIRD BRAIN, YOU WASTED THIS ENTIRE WEEK IN THE LIBRARY.

WE HAVE TO GIVE OUR REPORT ON MONDAY. YOU'D BETTER BUST YOUR BUTT OVER THE WEEKEND, OR I'M TELLING THE TEACHER YOU DIDN'T DO ANY WORK. GOT IT?

...WELL, WHAT DO YOU SAY?! AM I GETTING THROUGH TO YOU?? THIS IS IMPORTANT!

GRONK! GRIBBLE GOK! GAK GORK! GOONK!!

OUR HERO REGARDS THE STRANGE ALIEN. ...IT SEEMS TO BE TRYING TO COMMUNICATE.

CALVIN, TELEPHONE!

WHY AREN'T YOU AT THE LIBRARY?!?

WE HAVE TO GIVE OUR REPORT ON PLANET MERCURY TODAY. DID YOU DO YOUR HALF?

OF COURSE I DID. AND I'LL BET MY HALF MAKES YOUR HALF LOOK PATHETIC.

IT HAD **BETTER** BE GOOD... OR ELSE!

THE PLANET MERCURY
An Exhaustively Researched Report by Calvin

".. AND SO, THE PLANET MERCURY IS A HOT AND BARREN WORLD, THE CLOSEST TO OUR SUN."

AND TO TELL US ABOUT THE MYTHOLOGY OF MERCURY, HERE'S MY PARTNER, CALVIN.

THANK YOU, THANK YOU! HEY, WHAT A CROWD! YOU LOOK GREAT THIS MORNING... REALLY, I MEAN THAT! GO ON, GIVE YOURSELVES A HAND!

YOU KNOW, A FUNNY THING HAPPENED ON THE WAY TO THE LIBRARY YESTERDAY...

THIS ISN'T MY FAULT, MISS WORMWOOD!

THE PLANET MERCURY WAS NAMED AFTER A ROMAN GOD WITH WINGED FEET.

MERCURY WAS THE GOD OF FLOWERS AND BOUQUETS, WHICH IS WHY TODAY HE IS A REGISTERED TRADEMARK OF FTD FLORISTS.

WHY THEY NAMED A PLANET AFTER THIS GUY, I CAN'T IMAGINE.

... UM... BACK TO YOU, SUSIE.

BOY, YOU SHOULD'VE SEEN THE SPARKS FLY WHEN I GAVE MY HALF OF THE REPORT.

I'VE NEVER SEEN SUSIE SO MAD. SHE ACCUSED ME OF NOT DOING ANY RESEARCH AND CLAIMED I MADE UP THE WHOLE THING.

DID YOU?

HECK, NO. I JUST TOOK A FEW CREATIVE LIBERTIES.

AND THEY CALLED YOUR MOM OVER A FEW CREATIVE LIBERTIES?

GEEZ, YOU THINK *SUSIE* WAS MAD...

DON'T YOU HATE IT WHEN YOUR BOOGERS FREEZE?

HERE WE ARE, OVERLOOKING SUICIDE GULCH, ABOUT TO HURL OURSELVES DOWN AT BREAKNECK SPEED IN A SLED THAT HARDLY STEERS!

RISKING LIFE AND LIMB! LOOKING DEATH STRAIGHT IN THE EYE!

"WHY?" YOU ASK! WHY DO WE DO IT??

BECAUSE WE GET PAID, I HOPE.

BECAUSE IT'S THERE!

**Calvin and Hobbes** by WATTERSON

PLANET BOG — POOLS OF TOXIC CHEMICALS BUBBLE UNDER A CHOKING ATMOSPHERE OF POISONOUS GASES.

...BUT ASIDE FROM THAT, IT'S NOT MUCH LIKE EARTH.

WE FIND SPACEMAN SPIFF STRUGGLING ACROSS THE TERRAIN OF A DISTANT PLANET!

SUDDENLY THE GROUND BEGINS TO SHAKE! A CLOUD OF DUST APPEARS ON THE HORIZON! IT'S A ZORG!!

OUR HERO RUNS FOR COVER, BUT THE ZORG IS INSTANTLY UPON HIM!

SPIFF FIRES HIS BLASTER, BUT THE WEAPON IS USELESS AGAINST THE MONSTER!

THE FEARLESS SPACE EXPLORER IS TAKEN TO THE ZORG'S CAVE, WHERE HE DISCOVERS A VAT OF BOILING WATER! OH NO! OUR HERO IS ABOUT TO BE COOKED ALIVE!

SPIFF'S MIND RACES FURIOUSLY...

WELL? GET IN.

DON'T YOU WANT TO LEAN WAY, WAY OVER, AND TEST HOW HOT THE WATER IS?

LOOK, HOBBES, THE LATEST PERFECTION IN TECHNOLOGY.

A WATER PISTOL?

HECK, NO! THIS IS THE NEW, IMPROVED VERSION OF THE TRANSMOGRIFIER.

NOW YOU CAN TRANSMOGRIFY THINGS JUST BY POINTING AT THEM! SAY YOU DON'T LIKE THE COLOR OF YOUR BEDSPREAD. WELL, YOU JUST ZAP IT, AND PRESTO, IT'S AN IGUANA!

ONE CAN CERTAINLY IMAGINE THE MYRIAD OF USES FOR A HAND-HELD IGUANA MAKER.

IT DOESN'T *HAVE* TO BE AN IGUANA. IT CAN BE ANYTHING. SUPPOSE MOM'S GETTING ON OUR NERVES, FOR INSTANCE...

HOW DOES THIS TRANSMOGRIFIER GUN KNOW WHAT TO TRANSMOGRIFY SOMETHING INTO?

TELEPATHY.

THE GUN AUTOMATICALLY READS THE BRAIN WAVES YOU EMIT, AND TURNS THE OBJECT INTO WHATEVER YOU WANT.

THAT'S AMAZING.

WELL, IT TOOK ME ALL MORNING TO INVENT.

SO SAY I'M THINKING ABOUT A BIG SLAB OF GRILLED TUNA NOW...

WATCH WHERE YOU'RE POINTING THAT! WATCH WHERE YOU'RE POINTING THAT!

OK, LET'S TEST THIS TRANSMOGRIFIER GUN.

I WANT TO BE A PTERODACTYL, SO YOU THINK OF ONE AND POINT THE TRANSMOGRIFIER AT ME.

THIS WILL BE GREAT. I'LL TERRORIZE THE NEIGHBORHOOD AWHILE AND THEN YOU CAN TRANSMOGRIFY ME BACK TO A BOY WHEN THE NATIONAL GUARD COMES.

WHAT'S A PTERODACTYL? SOME KIND OF BUG?

NO NO! IT'S A BIG FLYING DINOSAUR! DON'T SHOOT IF YOU DON'T KNOW WHAT IT IS!!

DING DONG

I'LL GET IT.

HOBBES, QUICK! CLOSE THE CURTAINS AND HELP ME PROP FURNITURE AGAINST THE DOOR!

..IT'S ROSALYN!

DAD! DAD! WHERE DO YOU KEEP YOUR GUNS? GET OUT THE MAGNUM!

I DON'T HAVE ANY GUNS. WHAT'S THE PROBLEM?

ROSALYN'S HERE AND SHE WON'T GO AWAY! WHY ON EARTH DON'T YOU HAVE ANY GUNS??

YOUR MOM AND I ARE GOING OUT. ROSALYN IS HERE TO BABY-SIT.

DON'T YOU REMEMBER? I TOLD YOU THAT THIS MORNING.

YOU JUST DON'T PAY ATTENTION. THAT'S WHY YOU NEVER KNOW WHAT'S GOING ON.

HOW ABOUT A WOODEN STAKE AND A MALLET? DO WE HAVE THAT?!

CAN YOU BELIEVE IT, HOBBES? MOM AND DAD ASKED ROSALYN TO BABY-SIT US!

THERE'S JUST ONE THING TO DO. WE'LL MAIL OUR-SELVES TO AUSTRALIA. CLIMB IN.

TO: OS RLYa

JUST PUT US OUT BY THE MAIL-BOX, MOM.

STOP BEING SILLY, CALVIN. WHERE'S ROSALYN? I THOUGHT YOU SAID SHE WAS HERE.

TO:S TR.a

AS FAR AS I KNOW, SHE'S STILL ON THE FRONT PORCH. WHY?

YOU DIDN'T EVEN LET HER IN?!

DING DONG DING DONG

COME IN, ROSALYN! I'M SORRY! WE DIDN'T REALIZE CALVIN HADN'T LET YOU IN.

THAT'S OK. IT WASN'T *TOO* COLD AND WET OUT.

WE'RE LATE. HELP YOURSELF TO ANYTHING IN THE FRIDGE. WE'LL SEE YOU AT TEN.

THE DOOR WAS JAMMED. REALLY. I COULDN'T GET IT OPEN.

BED.

HEY, DON'T FIX *THAT* FOR DINNER! DIDN'T MOM TELL YOU HOBBES AND I ARE ON A STRICT BIG MAC DIET? IT'S DOCTOR'S ORDERS!

OH, I'D BETTER CALL YOUR DOCTOR THEN!

OH, NO, SHE CALLED MY BLUFF! THE DOCTOR'S GONNA BE FURIOUS! BOY, ARE WE GOING TO GET IT!

"WE"?

I'M DIALING!

HELLO, DOCTOR? I'M CALLING ABOUT CALVIN'S DIETARY NEEDS.

..AT THE TONE, THE TIME WILL BE 6:27 AND 10 SECONDS. ∗BEEP∗

BAD NEWS, CALVIN. YOUR DOCTOR SAYS YOU SHOULD HAVE A SPOONFUL OF CASTOR OIL AND LIE DOWN ALL EVENING.

HE DID? REALLY? NO, HE DIDN'T. DID HE? WHAT'S CASTOR OIL?

MOM DOESN'T SET THE TABLE THIS WAY. MOM DOES IT A LOT BETTER.

THIS FOOD SMELLS FUNNY. THIS ISN'T THE WAY MOM FIXES IT. I LIKE IT THE WAY MOM DOES IT BETTER.

I'M NOT YOUR MOM, ALL RIGHT?!

NO KIDDING! MY MOM LOVES ME MORE THAN LIFE ITSELF, AND SHE LETS ME DO ANYTHING I WANT. NOT LIKE *YOU*, YOU NASTY OL' BARRACUDA.

I CAN'T BELIEVE I POSTPONED A DATE FOR THIS.

# Calvin and Hobbes by WATTERSON

"MY....DAD...IS... A ...BIG...". **HEY!**

I THINK WE'D BETTER GET THAT KID TO A PSYCHOLOGIST.

Hey, Calvin, guess what we're doing in gym today. We're wrestling!

Next period you'll be so covered with mat burns you'll need skin grafts! Ha ha ha! See ya then, twinky.

SIGHHHHH...

PHYSICAL EDUCATION IS WHAT YOU LEARN FROM HAVING YOUR FACE IN SOMEONE'S ARMPIT RIGHT BEFORE LUNCH.

KAPWIINGGG! IT'S CALVIN, THE HUMAN LIGHT PARTICLE!

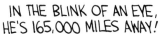

IN THE BLINK OF AN EYE, HE'S 165,000 MILES AWAY!

NOTHING IN THE UNIVERSE IS FASTER THAN CALVIN!

...I HOPE!

MUCH AS I LOVE MY "CHOCOLATE FROSTED CRUNCHY SUGAR BOMBS," THE BEST PART IS AFTER THE CEREAL IS GONE.

THAT'S WHEN YOU EAT THE LEFTOVER MILK THAT'S ALL SLUDGY FROM THE EXTRA SUGAR YOU ADDED.

SOMETIMES I EAT TWO OR THREE BOWLS OF THIS.

I CAN HEAR YOUR HEART RACING FROM HERE.

THEY MAKE THIS CEREAL WITH MARSHMALLOW BITS, TOO, BUT MOM WON'T BUY IT FOR ME.

# CALVIN AND HOBBES

by WATTERSON

IT'S FREEZING UPSTAIRS!

CAN I TAKE SOME LOGS UP TO MY ROOM?

HEY, YOU'RE ON MY SIDE OF THE BED.

THESE SHEETS ARE FREEZING!

YEAH, WELL... AAUGHH! YOUR FEET ARE LIKE ICE! GET AWAY FROM ME!

BUT MY SIDE'S ALL COLD!

WELL DON'T GET ME COLD! MOVE OVER!

SURE, YOU'VE GOT A FUR COAT! I'M JUST WEARING PAJAMAS.

QUIT PULLING THE BLANKETS, WILLYA?

I HARDLY HAVE ANY, YOU HOG! GIMME THOSE!

YOU'RE LETTING IN COLD AIR! QUIT IT! QUIT IT!

SERVES YOU RIGHT, MR. MOSTY-TOASTY! SEE WHAT IT'S LIKE BEING COLD!

YAAAAAH!!

EAT FEATHERS, FUZZ BALL!

WHAP OOF ZPOW

MOVE OVER. YOU'RE GETTING MY SIDE ALL HOT.

OPEN THE WINDOW. I'M ROASTING.

HEY, CALVIN! GUESS WHAT TIME IT IS!

WHY? WHAT TIME IS IT?

IT'S A VERY *SPECIAL* TIME!

OH BOY, OH BOY! WHAT TIME IS IT?

DO YOU *REALLY* WANT TO KNOW?

YES, YES! TELL ME! TELL ME! QUICK! PLEASE! YES!

**IT'S YOUR BATH TIME! OH BOY!!**

YOU KNOW HOW OLD PEOPLE ALWAYS WRITE TO DEAR ABBY, COMPLAINING THAT THEIR KIDS NEVER WRITE, CALL OR VISIT? THOSE LETTERS REALLY CRACK ME UP.

I HATE BEING A KID.

SOMEBODY'S ALWAYS TELLING YOU WHAT TO DO OR WHAT *NOT* TO DO. "DO THIS!" "STOP THAT!" DAY AFTER DAY.

YOU'RE LUCKY YOU'RE A TIGER.

WELL, WE TRY TO STAY HUMBLE, BUT LORD KNOWS IT'S HARD.

I WONDER IF I CAN GROW FANGS WHEN MY BABY TEETH FALL OUT.

I WISH *I* WAS A TIGER.

A COMMON LAMENT.

I'VE GOT AN IDEA! YOU CAN *TEACH* ME TO BE A TIGER! I'VE GOT SOME RED SLEEPERS I CAN WEAR! HANG ON!

SEE? WE CAN MAKE A TAIL BY STUFFING A KNEE SOCK AND PINNING IT ON MY REAR! THEN YOU CAN DRAW STRIPES ON MY FACE!

HMM... WHAT ABOUT FUR AND WHISKERS?

I HAVEN'T SHAVED FOR SIX YEARS. I SEEM TO BE CURSED WITH A THIN BEARD.

HOBBES, YOU'RE SUPPOSED TO BE TEACHING ME HOW TO BE A TIGER.

WE'VE BEEN SITTING IN THIS DUMB TREE ALL MORNING, AND YOU HAVEN'T TAUGHT ME HOW TO HUNT OR ANYTHING!

IT'S INSTINCT. YOU CAN'T TEACH THAT.

WELL IF YOU WON'T HELP, I'LL JUST GO LOOK UP "TIGER" IN THE ENCYCLOPEDIA.

AS LONG AS WE'RE GOING IN, LET'S FIX SOME SOUP AND SANDWICHES, OK?

YOU KNOW WHAT *YOU* ARE? A DISGRACE, THAT'S WHAT.

THIS BOOK SAYS TIGERS ARE SOLITARY AND SECRETIVE CREATURES.

TRUE. VERY TRUE.

SECRETIVE?

OH, SURE! YOU WOULDN'T *BELIEVE* SOME OF THE SECRETS I KNOW.

REALLY?? LIKE WHAT?

I CAN'T TELL YOU. THEY'RE SECRETS.

YOU CAN TELL ME! I WON'T BLAB! HONEST! TELL ME! PLEASE??

*BIG* SECRETS! *SECRET* SECRETS! BOY, IF YOU ONLY KNEW! MM-MM!

I DON'T BELIEVE YOU EVEN *HAVE* A SECRET.

THAT'S RIGHT. I DON'T.

YES YOU DO! TELL ME IT! PLEEEZE?

NO!

WHY NOT? WHY CAN'T YOU TELL ME??

IT'S ABOUT *YOU.*

AAAHHH! WHAT IS IT?? TELL ME! TELL ME!

I'VE SAID TOO MUCH ALREADY.

IF YOU WON'T TELL ME YOUR SECRET, I WON'T BE YOUR FRIEND ANY MORE.

I'LL GIVE YOU A HINT, HOW'S THAT?

OK! SHOOT.

THE FLEA MARKET.

"THE FLEA MARKET"?!? WHAT KIND OF LOUSY HINT IS *THAT*?

DO YOU KNOW HOW YOUR PARENTS GOT YOU?

I WAS... *WHY*? WHAT ARE YOU SAYING?

NO MORE HINTS.

I DON'T BELIEVE YOUR DUMB OL' SECRET ABOUT MY PARENTS GETTING ME AT A FLEA MARKET.

IT'S TRUE.

IT IS *NOT*, AND IF *ALL* YOUR SECRETS ARE LIES, YOU CAN JUST KEEP THEM TO YOURSELF.

YOU JUST DON'T WANT TO HEAR HOW LITTLE YOU WENT FOR.

OH, HUSH UP. THIS BOOK ALSO SAYS TIGERS WON'T SHARE THEIR TERRITORY WITH OTHER TIGERS.

I CAN SEE HOW OTHER TIGERS WOULD GET ON ONE'S NERVES.

A NICKEL. THAT'S HOW MUCH YOU COST.

THIS BOOK SAYS TIGERS ARE TERRITORIAL AND WON'T SHARE THEIR GROUND WITH OTHER TIGERS.

I GUESS WE'D BETTER DIVIDE UP THE WOODS THEN. THIS WILL BE MY TERRITORY, AND THAT WILL BE YOURS.

THIS ROCK WILL SEPARATE OUR TWO SIDES. AS ANOTHER TIGER, YOU ARE HEREBY BANISHED FROM THIS SIDE OF THE ROCK.

HA HA HA! LOOK WHAT I-I-I'M ♪ DOINGGG!

YOU CUT THAT OUT!

MY SIDE OF THE WOODS ABOUNDS IN NATURAL SCENIC SPLENDOR.

YOUR SIDE WALLOWS IN DECAY AND FILTH. MY TERRITORY IS INFINITELY SUPERIOR TO YOURS.

YOUR SIDE IS SMALLER.

HEY!

I'M HUNGRY.

WELL, YOU CAN'T CATCH ANYTHING IN MY TERRITORY. THAT'S WHAT THE BOOK SAYS.

WHAT DO TIGERS EAT IN THE WILD ANYWAY?

THEY CATCH BIG GROSS CATERPILLARS LIKE THAT ONE.

EWWW. IT'S GOT LITTLE SPIKES ALL OVER HIM. TIGERS REALLY EAT THESE?

BY THE TRUCK LOAD. THEY'RE GREAT.

LET ME SEE THE BOOK.

WHO ARE YOU GOING TO BELIEVE, SOME SILLY WRITER OR A REAL TIGER?

SO FAR, I HAVEN'T HAD MUCH FUN AS A TIGER.

I THOUGHT WE'D BE ROMPING AROUND THE WOODS LIKE WE ALWAYS DO, BUT IT TURNS OUT TIGERS DON'T SHARE THEIR TERRITORIES WITH OTHER TIGERS!

SO HERE WE ARE, SITTING ON OPPOSITE SIDES OF A BIG ROCK. WHAT A BLAST.

BEING A TIGER JUST ISN'T ALL IT'S CRACKED UP TO BE.

THAT'S NOT THE HALF OF IT. IT SAYS HERE WE'RE AN ENDANGERED SPECIES!

# CALVIN and HOBBES
### by WATTERSON

THE LATE CRETACEOUS PERIOD...
WHEN DINOSAURS RULED THE EARTH!

..AND CALVIN RULED THE DINOSAURS!

THE TERRIBLE TYRANNOSAURUS SINKS ITS TEETH INTO A TRICERATOPS!

TRIUMPHANT AGAIN, THE UNDISPUTED KING OF DINOSAURS LETS OUT A MIGHTY ROAR!

WITH SAVAGE FEROCITY, THE MONSTER BEGINS ITS FEAST! LIMB-SEVERING, BONE-CRUNCHING AND TENDON-SNAPPING, HE...

CALVIN! THAT'S DISGUSTING!

FOR HEAVEN'S SAKE, SLOW DOWN AND CHEW QUIETLY!

THE TERRIBLE TYRANNOSAURUS RESUMES EATING, MORTIFIED THAT SOMEONE MIGHT SEE HIM.

145

UH OH, I'LL BET HOBBES IS WAITING TO SPRING ON ME AS SOON AS I OPEN THE FRONT DOOR!

I KNOW! I'LL SNEAK AROUND BACK AND SURPRISE *HIM!*

HEH HEH! THERE HE IS, ALL READY TO POUNCE! WHAT A SUCKER!

I'M HOME!

I'VE GOT TO START LISTENING TO THOSE QUIET, NAGGING DOUBTS.

LIGHTNING FLASHES! THUNDER RUMBLES ACROSS THE SKY!

HORRIBLY, CALVIN HAS BEEN SEWN TOGETHER FROM CORPSES! A POWER SURGE FORCES BLOOD TO HIS BRAIN!

HE'S... HE'S *ALIVE!*

WELL, LOOK WHO'S UP AND ABOUT.

HELLO, SLEEPYHEAD.

..OGGG...

CALVIN WAKES UP STARING INTO THE EYES OF A BIG FROG.

SEEING CALVIN AWAKE, THE FROG SCRAMBLES DOWN AND FORCES OPEN CALVIN'S MOUTH!

CALVIN TRIES TO FIGHT, BUT THE SLIPPERY AMPHIBIAN INSTANTLY SLIDES IN AND IS SWALLOWED! HOW DISGUSTING!

I DON'T FEEL GOOD.

YOU SOUND AWFUL. YOU'VE GOT A FROG IN YOUR THROAT.

CALVIN THE ELEPHANT WANDERS THE AFRICAN PLAIN.

AT FIVE TONS, HE IS THE LARGEST LAND MAMMAL!

HIS DEAFENING CALL SHATTERS THE EARLY-MORNING TRANQUILITY!

AHH! LUNCH, MY FAVORITE MEAL! AND TODAY'S LUNCH IS *EXTRA* SPECIAL!

EVER SINCE THE WEATHER GOT WARM I'VE BEEN SWATTING FLIES AND SAVING THEM IN A JAR.

FINALLY I GOT ENOUGH BUGS TO MASH THEM INTO A GOOEY PASTE WITH A SPOON.

I CALL IT "BUG BUTTER." CARE FOR A TASTE?

TELL ME, CALVIN, DO YOU HAVE ANY FRIENDS AT *ALL*?

OK, YOU'VE ALL READ THE CHAPTER, SO WHO CAN TELL ME WHAT'S IMPORTANT ABOUT THE BATTLE OF LEXINGTON?

ANYONE?

CALVIN, HOW ABOUT YOU?

HARD TO SAY, MA'AM. I THINK MY CEREBELLUM JUST FUSED.

HEY, MOM, CAN WE GO OUT FOR HAMBURGERS TONIGHT?

NOT TONIGHT, DEAR.

AW, MOM! WHY NOT?

BECAUSE I'M ALREADY FIXING SOMETHING FOR DINNER.

YEAH... I KNOW.

# Calvin and Hobbes

by WATTERSON

YAWWNN

DESPITE THAT AMAZING DISPLAY OF CUNNING, REFLEX AND PHYSICAL PROWESS, YOUR TAIL STILL HAS A DEATH GRIP ON YOUR BUTT.

COULD YOU STOP THE ROOM, PLEASE? I'D LIKE TO GET OFF.

WATTERSON

BAD NEWS ON YOUR POLLS, DAD. YOU DROPPED ANOTHER FIVE POINTS.

IT SEEMS THAT ALTHOUGH YOUR RECOGNITION FACTOR IS HIGH, THE SCANDALS OF YOUR ADMINISTRATION CONTINUE TO HAUNT YOU.

SCANDALS? WHAT SCANDALS?!

BEDTIMEGATE AND HOMEWORKGATE COME READILY TO MIND.

INSTANCES OF TRUE LEADERSHIP. HISTORY WILL VINDICATE ME.

I WONDER WHAT MY NEW DAD WILL LOOK LIKE.

YOU'LL BE GLAD TO KNOW I'VE ANALYZED YOUR POOR SHOWING IN THE POLLS.

I'LL BET.

SEE, YOUR RECORD IN OFFICE IS MISERABLE AND THE CHARACTER ISSUE IS KILLING YOU. YOUR BASIC APPROVAL RATING AMONG SIX-YEAR-OLDS HARDLY REGISTERS.

IF ANYONE EVER NEEDED A SLICK AD CAMPAIGN, IT'S YOU.

LET ME GUESS WHAT YOU HAVE IN MIND.

"THE *NEW* DAD" I CALL IT.

I THINK THE IMAGE WE NEED TO CREATE FOR YOU IS, "REPENTANT, BUT LEARNING."

YOU KNOW, SHOW SOME HUMILITY, AND PRESENT YOURSELF AS A REGULAR GUY TRYING TO LEARN THE ROPES OF A DIFFICULT JOB.

DIFFICULT DOESN'T BEGIN TO DESCRIBE IT.

I WORKED UP SOME SLOGANS. SEE WHAT YOU THINK.

"DAD—GRADUALLY, HE CATCHES ON." "VOTE DAD! *THIS* TIME, HE'LL DO BETTER." "TO FORGIVE IS DIVINE—VOTE DAD IN '88."

I GET THE IDEA, CALVIN.

IF YOU WANT TO STAY DAD, YOU'VE GOT TO POLISH YOUR IMAGE.

MY IMAGE.

RIGHT. SEE, NOW EVERYONE THINKS YOU'RE INSENSITIVE TO THE LEGITIMATE NEEDS OF MINORS.

A FEW MAGNANIMOUS GESTURES WHILE IN OFFICE NOW MIGHT BE IN ORDER. IF YOUR MIND'S GONE BLANK, I HAVE SOME SUGGESTIONS.

OH, THE SUSPENSE.

FOR EXAMPLE, YOU MIGHT REPEAL MANDATORY SCHOOL ATTENDANCE. THAT ALONE COULD ROCKET YOU TO VICTORY.

MUCH AS I APPRECIATE YOUR OFFER, I DON'T THINK I NEED AN IMAGE CONSULTANT.

I PREFER TO LET THE WISDOM OF MY WORDS AND DEEDS SPEAK FOR THEMSELVES.

IN THAT CASE, YOU'LL HAVE A LOT OF TIME TO WRITE YOUR MEMOIRS.

WE'LL SEE. NOW IT'S PAST YOUR BEDTIME.

"DAD BURIED IN LANDSLIDE! JUBILANT THRONGS FILL STREETS! STUNNED FATHER INCONSOLABLE— DEMANDS RECOUNT!"

GOOD NIGHT.

EIGHT... NINE... TEN! HERE I COME, READY OR NOT!

ALL RIGHT, GIVE 'EM BACK!

155

# CALVIN AND HOBBES
by WATTERSON

YES, YOU CAN CERTAINLY SEE FAR FROM UP HERE.

I CALL THIS "LOOKOUT" HILL.

I CALL IT "LOOKOUT" HILL BECAUSE THAT'S WHAT YOU YELL WHENEVER WE GO DOWN IT.

YOU KNOW, SOMETIMES IT SEEMS THINGS GO BY TOO QUICKLY.

WE'RE SO BUSY WATCHING OUT FOR WHAT'S JUST AHEAD OF US THAT WE DON'T TAKE THE TIME TO ENJOY WHERE WE ARE.

DAYS GO BY AND WE HARDLY NOTICE THEM. LIFE BECOMES A BLUR.

OFTEN IT TAKES SOME CALAMITY TO MAKE US LIVE IN THE PRESENT.

THEN SUDDENLY WE WAKE UP AND SEE ALL THE MISTAKES WE'VE MADE, BUT IT'S TOO LATE TO CHANGE ANYTHING.

IT'S LIKE... ...IT'S LIKE...

IT'S LIKE WHAT?

IT'S LIKE SOMETHING... I JUST CAN'T THINK OF IT.

HEY, SUSIE, GUESS WHAT I HAVE IN MY HANDS!

IS IT DISGUSTING?

UM... ..WELL...

IS IT SOME CREEPY, GOOEY THING THAT NO ONE IN HIS RIGHT MIND WOULD EVER, EVER WANT TO LOOK AT?

UH... I. SUPPOSE THAT DEPENDS ON YOUR POINT OF VIEW...

FORGET IT. I'M NOT GUESSING.

YOU MIGHT AS WELL. YOU'RE NINE-TENTHS THERE.

MOM, WAS I EVER A GRUB?

A WHAT?

YOU KNOW, A LARVA. DID I REALLY PUPATE AT AGE TWO?

DON'T BE DISGUSTING! OF COURSE NOT! WHERE DID YOU EVER GET THAT AWFUL IDEA?!

YOU SHOULD GET YOUR STORIES STRAIGHT WITH MOM, MR. BRITANNICA!

HOW CAN YOU STAND THESE CARTOONS?

THEY'RE JUST HALF-HOUR COMMERCIALS FOR TOYS. AND WHEN THEY'RE NOT BORING, THEY'RE PREACHY.

AND THESE CHARACTERS DON'T EVEN *MOVE*. THEY JUST STAND AROUND BLINKING! WHAT KIND OF CARTOON IS *THAT*?

MEET MY DAD, THE GENE SISKEL OF SATURDAY MORNING TV.

# CALVIN and HOBBES

by WATTERSON

**C'MON, HOBBES. LET ME UP INTO THE TREE FORT.**

**SAY THE PASSWORD.**

**NO! YOU KNOW IT'S ME! LET ME UP!**

**YOU MAY BE SOME OTHER KID IN DISGUISE.**

**IT'S *ME*, CALVIN! LET ME UP, YOU HAIRBALL BARFER!**

**AN INSULT! WELL, YOU CAN JUST STAY DOWN THERE *FOREVER*, MR. STINKER.**

**OH, NO! HERE COMES SUSIE! LET ME UP QUICK, SO WE CAN THROW THINGS AT HER! HURRY! LET DOWN THE ROPE!**

**LA DE DA DUM DOO ♪♫**

**SHE'S COMING! QUICK! LET DOWN THE ROPE! I'M SORRY I INSULTED YOU! OK? SEE, I SAID I WAS SORRY! CAN'T YOU LET DOWN THE ROPE?!**

**YOU HAVE TO SAY THE PASSWORD.**

**..*Verse Seven:* TIGERS ARE PERFECT, THE *E*-PIT-O-ME OF GOOD LOOKS AND GRACE AND QUIET...UH..UM..DIGNITY.**

**I WAS GOING TO ASK YOU TO COME OVER AND PLAY HOUSE, BUT I THINK YOU'D BE A WEIRD EXAMPLE FOR OUR CHILDREN.**

**ONE OF THESE DAYS I'M GOING TO MAKE YOU INTO A RUG! YOU HEAR ME?? A RUG!**

162

GOSH, LOOK AT ALL THE DINOSAUR BONES WE DISCOVERED.

LET'S GLUE THEM TOGETHER SO WE CAN SEE HOW THEY FIT. THEN YOU CAN DRAW A RECONSTRUCTION OF THE ACTUAL DINOSAUR.

AFTER THAT, WE'LL WRITE UP OUR FINDINGS, AND GET THEM PUBLISHED IN A SCIENTIFIC JOURNAL.

THEN WE'LL WIN THE NOBEL PRIZE, GET RICH, AND GO ON TALK SHOWS.

WHAT ABOUT BABES? WHEN DO WE GET THOSE?

WELL, HERE'S THE COMPLETE SKELETON AS NEAR AS *I* CAN FIGURE OUT.

TRY TO DRAW THE DINOSAUR AS IT REALLY LOOKED WITH MUSCLES AND SKIN.

RIGHT.

WHAT'S IT DOING? WHISTLING?

YOU TELL ME. MAYBE IT'S PUCKERING UP.

SEE THE DINOSAUR SKELETON WE DISCOVERED AND ASSEMBLED?

I'M GOING TO CALL THE NATURAL HISTORY MUSEUM AND TELL THEM THEY CAN HAVE IT FOR TEN BILLION DOLLARS.

THOSE ARE ...UM... PECULIAR BONES.

DO YOU THINK I SHOULD ASK FOR MORE MONEY?

THAT'S NOT *QUITE* WHAT I MEANT.

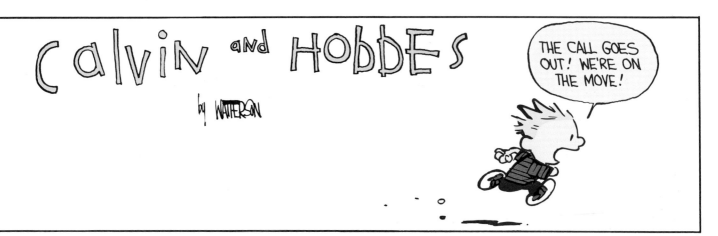

# Calvin and Hobbes

by WATTERSON

THE CALL GOES OUT! WE'RE ON THE MOVE!

UP THROUGH THE WINDING MAZE! FASTER! FASTER!

CALVIN SCRAMBLES UP THE GRAINY TUNNEL!

OUT HE POPS INTO THE BLINDING SUN! CALVIN THE ANT RUSHES DOWN THE HILL TO THE BRICK WALK!

OTHER ANTS RUSH AROUND HIM IN THEIR MAD HURRY! CALVIN TRIES TO KEEP UP!

AT LAST HE REACHES THE MONSTROUS DEAD CATERPILLAR! WITHOUT PAUSING, HE HOISTS IT UP!

THE QUEEN DEMANDS HIS TIRELESS TOIL! CALVIN IS BACK OFF TO THE ANT-HILL AS FAST AS HE CAN GO!

WORK, WORK, WORK! THAT'S ALL I'M GOOD FOR AROUND HERE!

I HARDLY THINK PICKING UP YOUR ROOM ONCE IN A WHILE QUALIFIES YOU AS A SLAVE.

# calvin and Hobbes
by WATTERSON

THIS IS CALVIN, YOUR CAPTAIN, SPEAKING...

...JUST TO REASSURE YOU THAT, YES, THERE IS SOMEONE UP FRONT.

CALVIN PILOTS THE JET AIRLINER ACROSS THE COUNTRY AT 35,000 FEET.

HE IS GIVEN CLEARANCE TO LAND. BUT WHAT'S THIS? A PLANE FROM A RIVAL AIRLINE IS MAKING FOR THE SAME RUNWAY TO SHAVE PRECIOUS MINUTES OFF ITS SCHEDULE!

IT'S A 600-MPH GAME OF CHICKEN! CALVIN PULLS BACK ON THE THROTTLE AND LURCHES AHEAD!

THE OTHER PILOT TRIES TO CUT CALVIN OFF WITH A SUDDEN DROP IN ALTITUDE!

CALVIN SWITCHES ON THE "FASTEN SEAT BELT" LIGHT IN THE CABIN, AND DOES A BARREL ROLL!

AT 5 Gs, CALVIN HOPES NOT TO BLACK OUT!

AS THEY CLOSE IN ON THE RUNWAY, THE OTHER PILOT HAS NO CHOICE BUT TO PULL UP AND CIRCLE AROUND AGAIN! CALVIN WINS!

HEY, MOM, IS IT TRUE I COULD GET A PILOT'S LICENSE AT AGE 14?

NO.

**HOBBES!** YOU'VE GOT TO HELP ME! I'M IN BIG TROUBLE!

WHAT'S THE MATTER?

YOU KNOW HOW DAD SAID I COULD USE HIS BINOCULARS AS LONG AS I WAS EXTRA CAREFUL WITH THEM? WELL, I JUST BROKE THEM BY ACCIDENT!

NOW I NEED SOME ADVICE. SHOULD I RUN AWAY, OR COMMIT HARA-KIRI?

OVER THE BINOCULARS?

YEAH.

MAYBE BOTH.

GEEZ, I CAN'T BELIEVE I BROKE DAD'S BINOCULARS! HE'LL BLOW EVERY CAPILLARY IN HIS BODY!

DAD SAID I HAD TO BE VERY, VERY CAREFUL WITH THEM, AND WHAT DO I DO? I GO AND BREAK THEM. HE'LL FLAY ME ALIVE!

HOW DID YOU DO IT, ANYWAY?

I JUST DROPPED THEM.

AND THEY BROKE?

WELL, I WAS TOSSING THEM TO MYSELF AT THE TIME, AS I RAN DOWN THE SIDEWALK.

HOW MUCH MONEY DO YOU HAVE, HOBBES? MAYBE WE CAN BUY DAD A NEW PAIR OF BINOCULARS BEFORE HE GETS HOME.

I'VE GOT THIRTY...NO, THIRTY-FIVE CENTS.

GREAT. I'VE GOT FOUR DOLLARS. LET'S CALL THE STORE.

HELLO? I'D LIKE TO KNOW HOW MUCH A GOOD PAIR OF BINOCULARS COSTS.

ONE TO SIX HUNDRED DOLLARS?! DO YOU HAVE ANY IDEA WHAT MY DAD'S GOING TO *DO* TO ME?!?

HE WON'T STOP AT KILLING YOU, THAT'S FOR SURE. UH UH.

I HAD NO *IDEA* BINOCULARS WERE SO EXPENSIVE! WE'RE DOOMED! WE'RE DOOMED!

"WE"?

WHY IN THE WORLD DID DAD LET ME USE ANYTHING SO *VALUABLE*?! HE SHOULD'VE *KNOWN* I'D BREAK THEM! HE MUST'VE BEEN OUT OF HIS MIND! THIS IS ALL *HIS* FAULT!

WHAT AM I GONNA *DO*!?

I SUPPOSE YOU *COULD* JUST TELL HIM WHAT HAPPENED...

..AND MAKE MY GETAWAY WHEN THE CORONARY HITS? SAY, *THAT'S* AN IDEA!

MAYBE WE COULD *GLUE* DAD'S BINOCULARS BACK TOGETHER AND HE WOULDN'T EVEN NOTICE! YOU THINK?

IT DEPENDS. WAS THE CASING JUST CHIPPED A LITTLE, OR DID THE LENS ITSELF GET CRACKED?

WELL, MAYBE YOU'D BETTER LOOK AT IT.

DON'T SNEEZE.

MAYBE YOU SHOULD TELL YOUR *MOM* ABOUT THE BINOCULARS, AND SHE CAN HELP SOMEHOW.

TELL MOM?!? ARE YOU CRAZY?? NO WAY!

WHY NOT? YOU'VE GOT TO TELL *SOMEONE*. MAYBE SHE CAN THINK OF SOMETHING.

AT TIMES LIKE THESE, ALL MOM CAN THINK OF IS HOW LONG SHE WAS IN LABOR WITH ME.

LOOK AT DAD, CALMLY EATING HIS DINNER AS IF NOTHING WAS WRONG.

I KNOW HIM. HIS "DAD RADAR" IS BEEPING LIKE CRAZY. HE KNOWS I BROKE *SOMETHING*, HE JUST DOESN'T KNOW *WHAT*. HE CAN'T NAIL ME UNTIL HE KNOWS FOR SURE. HE'LL JUST WAIT. I KNOW HIM.

HE'S GOING TO JUST SIT THERE EATING AND LET ME STEW IN MY OWN GUILT. HE FIGURES SOONER OR LATER I'LL CRACK.

CALVIN?

AAUGH! I DID IT! I DID IT! I'M SORRY! I DIDN'T MEAN TO!!

..PASS THE UH.. ..THE UH ...

YOU *BROKE* THE BINOCULARS?!

DIDN'T I TELL YOU TO BE EXTRA, EXTRA CAREFUL WITH THEM?? ISN'T THAT EXACTLY WHAT I SAID?! WELL?!

THOSE BINOCULARS WERE BRAND NEW! HAVE YOU NO RESPECT FOR OTHER PEOPLE'S PROPERTY.?◌

I HAVE AN IDEA, DAD. LET'S PRETEND I ALREADY FEEL TERRIBLE ABOUT IT, AND THAT YOU DON'T NEED TO RUB IT IN ANY MORE.

I DIDN'T *MEAN* TO BREAK YOUR BINOCULARS, DAD. IT WAS AN ACCIDENT.

(SNIFF) I'M REALLY SORRY. I FELT LIKE I WAS GOING TO BARF ALL AFTERNOON.

WELL, I'M SORRY I YELLED AT YOU LIKE I DID. I SHOULDN'T HAVE BEEN SO ANGRY.

AFTER ALL, IT WAS JUST A PAIR OF BINOCULARS. IN THE BIG SCHEME OF THINGS, THAT'S REALLY NOT SO BAD.

(SNIFF) REALLY?

SURE. ...IN ANOTHER TEN YEARS, YOU'LL PROBABLY BE WRECKING MY *CAR*.

# CALVIN AND HOBBES by WATTERSON

ZZZZZZZZZZZZZZ

FILTH! CONTAMINATION! PESTILENCE! HA HA HA!

OF ALL LIVING CREATURES, FEW ARE MORE REPULSIVE THAN CALVIN THE BUG!

HE EXISTS ONLY TO SUCK BLOOD AND TRANSMIT PARASITIC DISEASE!

SEARCHING FOR SOMEONE TO INFECT, CALVIN FLIES LOW OVER THE PICNIC TABLE!

INGREDIENTS: SALT,

HIS SENSITIVE ANTENNAE PICK UP THE SCENT OF HUMAN FLESH!

TOUCHING DOWN, CALVIN INSERTS HIS NEEDLELIKE PROBOSCIS INTO A VEIN! PROTOZOANS IN HIS SALIVA QUICKLY INDUCE PLAGUE!

WILL YOU STOP THAT AWFUL SLURPING?! YOU'RE MAKING ME SICK!

YOU KNOW WHAT WE NEED, HOBBES? WE NEED AN ATTITUDE.

AN ATTITUDE?

YEAH. YOU CAN'T BE COOL IF YOU DON'T HAVE AN ATTITUDE.

REALLY?

SURE. THEY'RE ALL THE RAGE. NOW WHAT KIND OF ATTITUDE COULD *WE* HAVE?

WE COULD BE COURTEOUSLY DEFERENTIAL.

OH, GOOD. THAT'S *REAL* COOL.

I'VE DECIDED TO BE A FATALIST.

ALL EVENTS ARE PREORDAINED AND UNALTERABLE. WHATEVER WILL BE WILL BE. THAT WAY, IF ANYTHING BAD HAPPENS, IT'S NOT MY FAULT. IT'S FATE.

TRIP

WAUGH

TOO BAD YOU WERE FATED TO DO THAT.

*THAT WASN'T FATE!*

DO YOU THINK GROWN-UPS WILL HAVE THE WORLD FIXED UP BY THE TIME THEY HAND IT OVER TO US?

NOT THE WAY THEY'RE GOING.

THAT'S WHAT *I* THOUGHT.

I GUESS THAT MEANS IT'S UP TO *US* THEN.

SOMEHOW, I'M NOT REASSURED.

HA! WHEN *I'M* PRESIDENT, I'LL HAVE THINGS WHIPPED INTO SHAPE IN NO TIME.

WELL, HERE WE ARE! HOME AWAY FROM HOME!

OK, CALVIN, YOU GET OUT WITH YOUR MOM, AND I'LL HAND OUR GEAR TO YOU.

NOW DON'T DROP THIS. IT'S VERY...

OOPS.

PLOONK

DON'T WORRY, DAD. IT'S ONLY ABOUT TEN FEET DEEP. I CAN SEE THE CAMERA AND EVERYTHING.

I AM GOING TO FEED YOU TO THE SEA GULLS, KID.

DEAR, YOU CAME HERE TO RELAX.

GOSH, THIS WATER'S COLD! HERE, THAT'S ALL I COULD FIND DOWN THERE. GO GET ME A TOWEL, CALVIN.

IT NEVER FAILS. THE ONE BAG THE KID DUMPS IN THE DRINK HAS ALL THE FRAGILE AND PERISHABLE ITEMS IN IT.

WELL, THE WEEK CAN ONLY IMPROVE FROM HERE.

ONE WOULD LIKE TO THINK SO.

HEY, DAD, DID YOU MEAN TO STACK THE TACKLE BOX AND ALL THIS ON YOUR GLASSES?

BOY, DON'T GO NEAR DAD. WHAT A GROUCH!

I DON'T SEE WHY HE CAN'T BE CIVIL JUST BECAUSE I ACCIDENTALLY DROPPED A DUFFEL BAG OVERBOARD AND HE BROKE HIS GLASSES.

ARE YOU GOING TO TELL HIM HE LEFT THE CAR LIGHTS ON BACK WHERE WE GOT THE CANOE?

I THINK YOU SHOULD TELL HIM.

HEY, MOM, DAD AND I ARE GOING FISHING. DON'T YOU WANT TO COME ALONG?

UGGH, NO. THE LAST THING I WANT TO SEE AT THIS UNGODLY HOUR IS A BUNCH OF SLIMY FISH GASPING AND FLOPPING IN THE SLOP AT THE BOTTOM OF A BOAT.

ALL *I'D* LIKE TO SEE IS A DECENT NEWSPAPER, A FRESH MUFFIN AND A POT OF REAL COFFEE.

WHY'D WE EVER COME *HERE* THEN?

GO ASK CONAN THE BARBARIAN.

C'MON, CALVIN. I'LL TEACH YOU TO PUT A WORM ON A HOOK.

AHHH, WHAT A DAY!

UP AT DAWN! FRESH AIR! TRANQUILITY! NO DEMANDS, NO PHONES, NO PRESSURE!

THE WHOLE DAY IS ONE'S OWN! ISN'T THIS GREAT? ISN'T THIS THE LIFE?

SPACEMAN SPIFF, A PRISONER ON THE ZOG SLAVE GALLEY, PLANS HIS DARING OVERBOARD ESCAPE!

AHH, WHAT A DAY!

GOSH, I COULD LOOK AT THE STARS ALL NIGHT.

WITHOUT THE STREETLIGHTS OR POLLUTION HERE, IT SEEMS LIKE YOU CAN SEE FOREVER INTO SPACE.

SNAP    CRUNCH

OF COURSE, IF YOU'VE SEEN ONE STAR, YOU'VE SEEN THEM ALL.

TRUE, TRUE. SHALL WE MOSEY ON BACK TO THE TENT?

LOOK, MOM, THE WATER IS UP TO MY KNEES!

SEE? SEE? LOOK, MOM! THE WATER'S UP TO MY KNEES! SEE? LOOK WHERE THE WATER IS!

NOW LOOK! THE WATER IS *HIGHER* THAN MY KNEES! SEE? LOOK, MOM! SEE?

I'M ENTHRALLED, CALVIN.

YOU'RE NOT EVEN *LOOKING!*

WHATCHA DOIN', DAD? PAINTING A PICTURE?

YEP.

WHAT'S THAT THING? A BRONTOSAURUS WITH RABIES?

IT'S THAT ISLAND OVER THERE.

OH.

HOW FAR CAN YOU SEE WITHOUT YOUR GLASSES? CAN YOU SEE *ME?*

WHEN I LOOK UP, I'D BETTER NOT BE ABLE TO.

HI, MOM!

MM.

DAD'S PAINTING A PICTURE, BUT IT'S NOT COMING OUT SO HOT, AND HE'S IN A REALLY STINKY MOOD. IT'S LIKE, I ASKED HIM ONE LITTLE QUESTION AND HE NEARLY BIT MY HEAD OFF! I MEAN, IT'S NOT AS IF *I* RUINED HIS LOUSY PICTURE, RIGHT? WHY SHOULD...

CALVIN, CAN'T YOU SEE I'M TRYING TO READ?

EVER NOTICE HOW TENSE GROWN-UPS GET WHEN THEY'RE RECREATING?

THERE'S NOTHING TO *DO* HERE.

THAT'S SORT OF THE POINT, DON'T YOU THINK? IT'S GOOD TO STOP RUNNING AROUND.

SOMETIMES ONE SHOULD JUST LOOK AT THINGS AND THINK ABOUT THINGS, WITHOUT *DOING* THINGS.

YOU'RE CERTAINLY THE EXPERT ON *THAT*.

WHAT I LIKE IS WHEN YOU'RE LOOKING AND THINKING AND LOOKING AND THINKING....AND SUDDENLY YOU WAKE UP.

MOM, CAN HOBBES COME IN SWIMMING WITH ME?

I DON'T THINK HE'D BETTER, CALVIN.

WHY NOT?

UM... TIGERS DON'T SWIM VERY WELL.

THEY DON'T?

FRANKLY, I'M NOT SURE YOUR MOM KNOWS SO MUCH ABOUT TIGERS.

LOOK, WE JUST WANT TO AVOID AN ARGUMENT, RIGHT?

OK, CALVIN, START PACKING UP. WE'RE GOING HOME.

FINALLY!

NOW, NOW. THESE LITTLE OUTINGS ARE VALUABLE EXPERIENCES.

YEAH? HOW?

THEY GIVE US A CHANCE TO BE TOGETHER AS A FAMILY AND LEARN ABOUT OURSELVES.

LIKE HOW WE CAN'T STAND BEING IN SUCH CLOSE PROXIMITY WITH ONE ANOTHER THIS LONG?

EXACTLY.

THIS HAS GOT TO BE A DREAM.

WHENEVER YOU FALL FROM TWO MILES UP IN THE SKY, YOU LOOK DOWN, GASP, AND SUDDENLY WAKE UP.

GASP!

GASP
GASP
GASP
GASP
GASP

I WONDER IF MY LIFE WILL FLASH BEFORE MY EYES.

THAT'S THE PROBLEM WITH BEING SIX YEARS OLD...

...MY LIFE WON'T TAKE VERY LONG TO WATCH.

MAYBE I CAN GET A FEW SLOW-MOTION REPLAYS OF THE TIME I SMACKED SUSIE UPSIDE THE HEAD WITH A SLUSHBALL.

SAY, I WONDER IF I HAVE ANY GUM IN MY POCKET. I COULD BLOW A BIG BUBBLE, AND...

NOPE, NO GUM. LET'S TRY *THIS* POCKET.

MY TRANSMOGRIFIER GUN!!

BOY, THESE THINGS COME IN HANDY ALL THE TIME.

I FORGOT ALL ABOUT MY TRANSMOGRIFIER GUN! NOW I HAVE NOTHING TO WORRY ABOUT!

I'LL JUST POINT IT AT MYSELF AND TRANSMOGRIFY! I'M SAFE!

ZAP

WHERE HAVE YOU BEEN?? I'VE BEEN CALLING AND CALLING. YOUR DINNER'S COLD, I'M SURE.

I DRIFTED AWAY ON MY BALLOON AND IT POPPED, BUT FORTUNATELY I HAD MY TRANSMOGRIFIER, SO AFTER I MISTAKENLY TURNED MYSELF INTO A SAFE, I TRANSMOGRIFIED INTO A LIGHT PARTICLE AND ZIPPED BACK HOME INSTANTANEOUSLY!

...OF COURSE, IF I'D KNOWN WE WERE HAVING THIS, I WOULDN'T HAVE HURRIED.

SOMETIME YOU SHOULD TRY TRANSMOGRIFYING YOURSELF INTO SOMEONE WHO OCCASIONALLY MAKES AN OUNCE OF SENSE.

CALVIN, I'D LIKE YOU TO PICK UP ALL THE STICKS AND FALLEN BRANCHES IN THE YARD, SO I CAN MOW IT.

WILL YOU PAY ME?

WELL... OK, I'LL PAY YOU A DOLLAR.

A DOLLAR? I WON'T DO IT FOR LESS THAN TWENTY-FIVE!!

IN A MINUTE YOU'LL DO IT FOR NOTHING, JUST BECAUSE I TOLD YOU TO.

...I'LL TAKE THE DOLLAR.

SMART KID.

CALVIN and HOBBES by WATTERSON

SPACEMAN SPIFF EXPLORES THE OUTERMOST REACHES OF THE UNIVERSE.

BY POPULAR REQUEST.

INTREPID EXPLORER SPACEMAN SPIFF LANDS ON AN UNCHARTED PLANET. WHAT STRANGE WONDERS WILL HE DISCOVER HERE?

SPIFF SETS OUT IN SEARCH OF SENTIENT LIFE!

WHAT A STRANGE PLANET THIS IS! ITS SURFACE IS SURPRISINGLY SOFT AND POROUS!

AND HERE CURIOUS GEYSERS BLAST HOT AIR!

SUDDENLY IT DAWNS ON HIM! SPIFF IS NOT ON THE PLANET'S SURFACE AT ALL! HE'S WALKING ON A RECLINING ALIEN!!

OUR HERO SETS HIS DEATH RAY BLASTER.

ZZ.. MMF HM?

193

# Calvin and Hobbes
### by WATTERSON

HERE'S "HAMSTER HUEY AND THE GOOEY KABLOOIE." YOU MIGHT LIKE THIS STORY.

YEAH? HOW GOOD CAN IT BE IF IT HASN'T BEEN MADE INTO AN ANIMATED TV SHOW?

I HOPE TONIGHT'S STORY ISN'T AS BORING AS *LAST* NIGHT'S WAS. IT PUT ME RIGHT TO SLEEP.

DON'T WORRY. *THIS* STORY WILL KEEP YOU UP ALL NIGHT.

REALLY? WHAT IS IT?

IT'S CALLED, "THE DISEMBODIED HAND THAT STRANGLED PEOPLE."

GOSH, THIS IS GREAT! HOW CREEPY! I *NEVER* GET A SCARY STORY! A DISEMBODIED HAND! WOW!

AND YOU KNOW WHAT'S *REALLY* SCARY? THEY NEVER FOUND IT! TO THIS DAY, NOBODY KNOWS WHERE THE HAND IS!

WATTERSON

IN FACT, THE HAND COULD...

OH NO!! THERE IT IS!

IT'S G-GOT ME!!

GAKK!!

..CALVIN?...
...CALVIN?..

I SHOULD'VE THOUGHT OF THAT YEARS AGO.

LET'S GO, CALVIN! WE'RE ALL READY!

BOY, I HAVEN'T BEEN TO THE ZOO IN AGES.

AND CALVIN'S NEVER BEEN. THIS WILL BE FUN.

I'VE BEEN TELLING HIM ABOUT IT ALL WEEK. HE'S SO EXCITED.

C'MON, CALVIN!

SO *WHERE* DO WE HAVE TO GO NOW?

BEATS *ME*. MOM AND DAD ARE ALWAYS DRAGGING US *SOME* DUMB PLACE.

HOW COME THE ALLIGATORS ARE IN THIS BIG PIT?

SO THEY DON'T GET OUT AND EAT PEOPLE.

DOES THE ZOO EVER THROW ANYONE IN?

DON'T BE SILLY. OF COURSE NOT.

HOW SOON UNTIL WE GO HOME?

LOOK! MONKEYS!

SEE HOW THEY USE THEIR TAILS AND FEET TO CLIMB?

ZOOS LET PEOPLE SEE HOW WILD ANIMALS REALLY BEHAVE.

HEY, LOOK WHAT *THAT* MONKEY'S DOING! RIGHT IN PUBLIC, TOO! HA HA! THAT'S GROSS! HOW COME *I'M* NOT ALLOWED TO DO THAT?!

COME LOOK AT THE BIRDS OVER HERE, CALVIN.

WHAT DO YOU THINK OF THE ZOO?

I THINK IT'S KIND OF DEPRESSING.

I ALWAYS FEEL SORRY FOR THE ANIMALS. THEY DON'T HAVE MUCH ROOM TO MOVE, OR ANYTHING TO DO.

THEY JUST SLEEP UNTIL THEY'RE FED.

THAT'S PRETTY MUCH ALL *YOU* DO.

YOU KNOW WHAT I MEAN.

HEY, THOSE KIDS ARE FEEDING THE ANIMALS!

MOM, CAN I GET SOME PEANUTS TO FEED THE ANIMALS?

I'M NOT YOUR MOM.

WHOOP!

ARE YOU LOST? WHAT DOES YOUR MOM LOOK LIKE?

FROM THE KNEES DOWN, SHE LOOKS JUST LIKE YOU.

GOSH, I FOLLOWED THAT LADY HALFWAY AROUND THE ZOO, THINKING SHE WAS MY MOM.

WHY DON'T MOMS WRITE THEIR NAMES ON THEIR CALVES SO THIS KIND OF THING WOULDN'T HAPPEN?

I WONDER WHERE I AM. AND WHERE'S HOBBES? I THOUGHT HE WAS RIGHT WITH ME.

UH OH. WHERE'S CALVIN?

WHY DO THESE LITTLE FAMILY TRIPS ALWAYS TURN OUT THIS WAY? I'M GOING TO SPEND MORE SATURDAYS AT THE OFFICE.

HERE'S HOBBES, BUT WHERE'S CALVIN?

I DON'T SEE HIM.

WHERE COULD HE HAVE GONE? WE JUST TURNED OUR BACKS FOR A MINUTE.

AND WHY DIDN'T HE TAKE HOBBES?

YOU STAY HERE IN CASE HE COMES BACK, AND I'LL GO LOOK FOR HIM.

OK. (SIGH)

BEING A PARENT IS WANTING TO HUG AND STRANGLE YOUR KID AT THE SAME TIME.

SHEESH. CALVIN COULD BE ANYWHERE IN THIS ZOO.

I HOPE HE AT LEAST HAS THE SENSE TO STAY PUT, WHEREVER HE IS.

WHERE WOULD THE LITTLE ROTTER GO IF HE WAS LOST AND SEPARATED FROM HIS STUFFED TOY?

HIS NAME IS HOBBES, AND HE'S... HEY, I'M TALKING TO YOU!!

TIGERS
Panthera tigris

I KNOW! MAYBE CALVIN'S AT THE TIGER PIT, SINCE HE LIKES TIGERS SO MUCH.

HA HA, MAYBE CALVIN'S *IN* THE TIGER PIT, SINCE HE LIKES TIGERS SO MUCH.

YOU FOUND HIM! THANK GOODNESS! WHERE WAS HE?

LOOKING AT THE TIGERS.

I FOLLOWED ANOTHER LADY, THINKING IT WAS MOM, AND THEN WHEN I REALIZED I WAS LOST, I WENT TO ASK THE TIGERS IF THEY'D SEEN HOBBES.

NEXT TIME YOU SHOULD ASK A *PERSON* FOR HELP.

...OH... THAT NEVER OCCURRED TO ME.

ONLY NEXT TIME, THERE WON'T *BE* A NEXT TIME, BECAUSE WE'RE JUST GOING TO TIE YOU TO A STAKE IN THE YARD EVERY WEEKEND.

DEAR!

A FAT LOT OF HELP YOUR COMPATRIOTS WERE, I MIGHT ADD.

---

DO YOU KNOW WHAT DAY IT IS?

NOPE. WHY?

OH, NO REASON. I WAS JUST CURIOUS.

I SURE LIKE SUMMER VACATION.

---

SO YOU WANT SOME WATER, HUH? WELL, I'VE GOT A BIG CAN OF IT HERE.

IT'S UP TO *ME* TO DECIDE IF YOU GET WATER OR NOT! *I* CONTROL YOUR FATE! YOUR VERY *LIVES* ARE IN MY HANDS!

WITHOUT *ME* YOU'RE AS GOOD AS DEAD! WITHOUT *ME*, YOU DON'T...

I GOT A HIT!

SAFE!

OK, THAT WAS A SINGLE. I HAVE A GHOST RUNNER HERE NOW, SO I CAN BAT AGAIN.

AND MY GHOST RUNNERS WHO *WERE* ON FIRST AND SECOND BASE ARE NOW ON SECOND AND THIRD, RIGHT?

NOPE. THEY'RE BOTH OUT.

OUT?!

MY GHOST OUTFIELDER TAGGED YOUR GHOST GOING TO THIRD, AND THREW TO MY GHOST SECOND BASEMAN. IT WAS A BRILLIANT DOUBLE PLAY.

THAT NEVER HAPPENED!

YOU'VE GOT TWO OUTS.

WELL, MY GHOST ON FIRST JUST STOLE HOME, SO I'VE GOT ANOTHER RUN! HA HA, SMARTY!

YEAH, WELL, ALL MY OUTFIELD GHOSTS JUST RAN IN AND BEAT THE TOBACCO JUICE OUT OF HIM.

HA! THE GHOST UMPIRE JUST SUSPENDED ALL YOUR GHOSTS FOR ETERNITY. THEY'RE OUT OF THE GAME.

HMPH! IF MY GHOSTS DON'T PLAY, *I* DON'T PLAY.

YOU FORFEIT THE GAME THEN! YOU LOSE AUTOMATICALLY IF YOU QUIT!

THE GHOST CROWD SUPPORTS ME. THEY'RE "BOO"-ING YOU!

SOMETIMES I WISH I LIVED IN A NEIGHBORHOOD WITH MORE KIDS.

# Calvin and Hobbes by WATTERSON

BOY, WHAT A BEAUTIFUL SUMMER MORNING, HUH, DAD? TOO BAD YOU CAN'T STAY HOME TO ENJOY IT.

WHEN YOU'RE OLD, YOU'LL BE SORRY YOU NEVER TOOK ADVANTAGE OF DAYS LIKE THESE, BUT OF COURSE, THAT'S FAR OFF, AND IN THE MEANTIME, THERE'S LOTS OF WORK TO BE DONE.

YEP, YOU'D BETTER GO TO WORK. HAVE A GOOD LONG DRIVE IN TRAFFIC. MAYBE YOU'LL GET HOME IN TIME TO WATCH THE SUN SET... IF YOU CAN STAY AWAKE. SO LONG!

GOLLY, I'D HATE TO HAVE A KID LIKE ME.

WHAT WOULD YOU DO IF I CREAMED YOU WITH THIS WATER BALLOON RIGHT NOW?

TAKE THE WORST THING YOU CAN IMAGINE, AND IMAGINE SOMETHING A HUNDRED TIMES WORSE THAN THAT.

YOU'D DO THAT?

NO, I'D DO SOMETHING EVEN WORSE.

HE PIQUED MY CURIOSITY.

BIP

WHEEEE.

203

WHAT ARE YOU DOING WITH ALL YOUR DAD'S TOOLS IN THE BATHROOM?

THIS FAUCET DRIPS, SO I'M GOING TO FIX IT.

*YOU'RE* GOING TO FIX IT?

THAT'S WHAT I SAID.

..AND YOU CAN KEEP YOUR COMMENTS TO YOURSELF, DR. DOOM.

I DIDN'T SAY ANYTHING.

FIXING A FAUCET IS EASY. ALL YOU DO IS TAKE IT APART, SEE WHAT'S LEAKING, PLUG IT UP, AND PUT IT BACK TOGETHER.

DOES YOUR MOM KNOW YOU'RE DOING THIS?

NOPE. IT'S GOING TO BE A SURPRISE.

AND WE ALL KNOW HOW SHE LOVES SURPRISES.

I CAN'T GET THIS HANDLE OFF. PASS ME THE HACKSAW, WILL YOU?

AREN'T YOU SUPPOSED TO TURN THE WATER OFF BEFORE YOU TAKE APART A FAUCET?

THAT'S THE PROBLEM I'M TRYING TO FIX, YOU MORON! I CAN'T TURN THE WATER OFF BECAUSE THE FAUCET LEAKS!

SHEESH, WHERE WERE *YOU* WHEN THEY WERE PASSING OUT BRAINS?

OH NO! AUGHH! ACKK!

I'LL GET YOU SOME PAPER AND CARBONS FOR YOUR WRITTEN APOLOGY.

WHAT'S ALL THAT WATER I HEAR? I'M COMING IN!

OH MY GOSH! ACKPBT! WHAT'S GOING ON?!? SPLUTB! BPLPTH!

THERE! I GOT THE WATER OFF. **ALL RIGHT, CALVIN, WHERE ARE YOU?!**

H-HI, DAD.

IT'S THE END OF THE WORLD, CALVIN.

LOOK AT THIS BATHROOM! WHAT ON EARTH WERE YOU *DOING*?!

NOTHING, DAD! I WAS JUST IN HERE LOOKING FOR SOME DENTAL FLOSS, WHEN *PLOOIE!* THE FAUCET HANDLE BLOWS SKY HIGH ALL BY ITSELF! IT... IT... UH...

WHAT I MEAN IS, HOBBES WAS FOOLING AROUND WITH YOUR TOOLS. I TRIED TO STOP HIM, BUT HE WOULDN'T LISTEN, AND SURE ENOUGH, HE WENT AND... AND...

ONE MORE TRY.

**ALIENS**, DAD! BIG, EVIL, BUG-EYED MONSTERS FROM PLUTO! THEY DID IT, AND MADE ME SWEAR NOT TO TELL!

BOY, DAD SURE BLEW HIS STACK *THAT* TIME, DIDN'T HE? WHAT A SOREHEAD!

LISTENING TO *HIM*, YOU'D THINK NOBODY IN THE WORLD HAD EVER NEEDED TO CALL A PLUMBER BEFORE. DAD'S GOT A JOB. HE CAN AFFORD IT.

DAD MAKES SUCH A BIG DEAL OUT OF EVERYTHING.

WHEN HE DOES, I SURE WISH YOU'D STOP TRYING TO PIN YOUR CRIMES ON *ME*.

OH, NOW *YOU'RE* GOING TO START IN ON ME *TOO*, HUH?

CALVIN and HOBBES by WATTERSON

DINOSAURS EVERYWHERE FLEE FOR THEIR LIVES!

CALVIN IS COMING!

THE LATE CRETACEOUS: THE LAST EPOCH OF THE MIGHTY DINOSAURS!

KING OF THE THUNDER LIZARDS IS THE FEARSOME CALVIN, THE TYRANNOSAURUS!

SEVEN TONS OF MUSCLE AND TEETH, HE SEARCHES FOR PREY!

CALVIN, FOR GOODNESS' SAKE, STOP STOMPING AROUND! YOU'RE DRIVING ME CRAZY!

OW!! CHOMP

HOW DID THE FEARSOME TYRANNOSAURUS BECOME EXTINCT? NOW WE KNOW!

WATTERSON

EVERYTHING FLOATS RANDOMLY IN THE ROOM! THERE'S NO GRAVITY!

CALVIN PUSHES OFF THE CEILING AT A SHARP ANGLE, AIMING FOR THE HALLWAY!

HE GLIDES WITH UNCHECKED MOMENTUM, TURNING HIMSELF TO BE ABLE TO PUSH OFF THE NEXT STATIONARY SURFACE.

C'MON, YOU! OUTSIDE! YOU'RE REALLY BOUNCING OFF THE WALLS TODAY.

AW, MOM.

EXTRA PANTS...

THREE SHIRTS, TWO SWEATERS, TWO SWEATSHIRTS...

ANOTHER PAIR OF PANTS...

STILL TRYING TO LEARN TO RIDE THAT BICYCLE, EH?

I DON'T NEED ANY COMMENTS FROM YOU.

A SHADOW FALLS OVER THE LARGE CITY SKYSCRAPERS!

IT'S A GIGANTIC ANT! WITH ONE FOOTSTEP, IT PULVERIZES THE ENTIRE DOWNTOWN! MILLIONS DIE INSTANTLY!

THE ANT BRUSHES THE CITY OFF THE MAP! PEOPLE FLOOD THE STREETS IN PANIC, ONLY TO BE SMASHED IN THE HORRIBLE WRECKAGE!

WELL... MAYBE I WON'T...

PLANET CALVIN MOVES ACROSS THE SOLAR SYSTEM.

NOBODY NOTICES UNTIL HIS ORBIT TAKES HIM DIRECTLY BETWEEN THE SUN AND EARTH.

CALVIN CAUSES A TOTAL SOLAR ECLIPSE! EARTH IS SHROUDED IN DARKNESS. HOW LONG WILL CALVIN STAY THERE?!

COULD YOU MOVE, PLEASE? YOU'RE IN MY LIGHT.

HA HA HAAA!

ELECTION DAY IS COMING UP. HAVE YOU DECIDED ON A RUNNING MATE?

A RUNNING MATE?

SURE. YOU CAN'T BE ELECTED DAD WITHOUT A MOM, RIGHT?

ARE YOU GOING TO KEEP THE MOM I'VE HAD, OR GET A *NEW* RUNNING MATE?

GEE...

BEDTIME, CALVIN.

OF COURSE I'LL STICK WITH YOUR MOM.

AWW...

I THINK RITUALS ARE IMPORTANT.

*MY* FAVORITE RITUAL IS EATING THREE BOWLS OF "CHOCOLATE FROSTED SUGAR BOMBS" AND WATCHING TV CARTOONS ALL SATURDAY MORNING.

AFTER A FEW HOURS, I'M SO OVERSTIMULATED I CAN'T SIT STILL OR EVEN THINK STRAIGHT.

SORT OF A TRANSCENDENTAL EXPERIENCE, HUH?

YEAH. I ACHIEVE A LOWER CONSCIOUSNESS.

ALL RIGHT, ALL RIGHT! I'M *GOING!*

HEY! LEGGO! I CAN WALK MYSELF! I JUST HAVE TO... *OK!* LOOK, I'M GOING! I'M GOING!

SURE, YOU THINK SCHOOL'S GREAT *NOW*, BUT IN A COUPLE OF HOURS YOU'LL *MISS* ME! YOU'LL SEE!

THERE GOES CALVIN OFF TO SCHOOL. HE SURE PUT UP A FUSS.

WELL, HE'LL HAVE FUN ONCE HE GETS THERE.

SEE, HE'S EVEN RUNNING NOW. HE'S ALL EXCITED ABOUT...

HEY! CALVIN, THE BUS STOP IS *THAT* WAY! COME BACK HERE!

I CAN'T BELIEVE I'M HERE WAITING TO GO TO SCHOOL. WHAT HAPPENED TO SUMMER?

GOSH, I COULDN'T *WAIT* FOR TODAY! SOON WE'LL BE MAKING NEW FRIENDS, LEARNING ALL SORTS OF IMPORTANT THINGS, AND...

WHAT'S THE MATTER WITH *YOU*??

YOUR BANGS DO A GOOD JOB OF COVERING UP THE LOBOTOMY STITCHES.

I PLEDGE ALLEGIANCE...

TO QUEEN FRAGG... AND HER MIGHTY STATE OF HYSTERIA...

IT'S GOING TO BE A LONG YEAR.

Hey, Calvin, you're on my swing. Get lost.

I'M NOT SCARED OF YOU, MOE.

Oh no?

NOPE. YOU'RE SO DUMB YOU PROBABLY NEVER THOUGHT ABOUT HOW A SPARROW'S SMALLER SIZE AND GREATER MANEUVERABILITY IS AN ADVANTAGE IN FIGHTING OFF BIG CROWS.

Yeah?

PUNCH

THOSE TV NATURE PROGRAMS WILL BE THE DEATH OF ME YET.

YES, CALVIN?

MAY I BE EXCUSED, PLEASE?

AGAIN?

I HAVE TO GO. BAD.

ALL RIGHT.

THANK YOU.

WHAT ARE *YOU* DOING HOME?!

I HAD TO GO.

# Calvin and Hobbes

by WATTERSON

SCHOOL'S OUT! FREE AT LAST!

AND JUST SIX PRECIOUS HOURS BEFORE BED TO FORGET EVERYTHING I LEARNED TODAY.

I HATE COMING HOME FROM SCHOOL. I NEVER KNOW IF HOBBES IS WAITING TO POUNCE ON ME.

MAYBE I CAN STAND OFF TO THE SIDE HERE, AND PUSH THE DOOR OPEN WITH A STICK.

I'M HOME!

KAPOW!

WHAT DO YOU DO, WAIT UNTIL YOU SEE THE WHITES OF MY EYES?!?

BOY, YOU SHOULD'VE *SEEN* THEM! THEY WERE AS BIG AS DINNER PLATES! HOO HOO HOO!

219

HAVE YOU BEEN READING THE PAPERS? GROWN-UPS REALLY HAVE THE WORLD FOULED UP.

ACID RAIN, TOXIC WASTES, HOLES IN THE OZONE, SEWAGE IN THE OCEANS, AND ON AND ON!

THE ONLY BRIGHT SIDE TO ALL THIS IS THAT EVENTUALLY THERE MAY NOT BE A PIECE OF THE PLANET WORTH FIGHTING OVER.

YOU'RE PACKING?

YEP. GET YOUR TOOTHBRUSH, HOBBES. WE'RE OUTTA HERE.

IT'S AN OUTRAGE HOW GROWN-UPS HAVE POLLUTED THE EARTH! I REFUSE TO INHERIT A SPOILED PLANET! I'M *LEAVING!*

REALLY? WHERE TO??

YOU KNOW, SOMETIMES YOU'RE A REAL LOAD TO HAVE AROUND.

I WAS JUST *ASKING!*

HOW ABOUT MARS? WE COULD GO THERE TO AVOID EARTH'S POLLUTION.

YEAH! IF WE GO *NOW*, WE CAN CLAIM IT AND KEEP EVERYONE ELSE OFF IT.

OK, IT'S SETTLED. MARS IT IS.

YOU FINISH PACKING. I'LL GO GET THE WAGON.

WE'RE GOING IN THE WAGON?

OF COURSE! WHAT DID *YOU* WANT TO DO? FLAP YOUR ARMS?

I GUESS I HADN'T THOUGHT ABOUT THAT PART.

OBVIOUSLY.

SPACE TRAVEL MAKES YOU REALIZE JUST HOW SMALL WE REALLY ARE.

WHEN YOU SEE EARTH AS A TINY BLUE SPECK IN THE INFINITE REACHES OF SPACE, YOU HAVE TO WONDER ABOUT THE MYSTERIES OF CREATION.

SURELY WE'RE ALL PART OF SOME GREAT DESIGN, NO MORE OR LESS IMPORTANT THAN ANYTHING ELSE IN THE UNIVERSE. SURELY EVERYTHING FITS TOGETHER AND HAS A PURPOSE, A REASON FOR BEING. DOESN'T IT MAKE YOU WONDER?

I WONDER WHAT HAPPENS IF YOU THROW UP IN ZERO GRAVITY.

MAYBE YOU SHOULD WONDER WHAT IT'S LIKE TO WALK HOME.

HANG ON! WE'RE COMING IN THROUGH MARS' ATMOSPHERE.

BONK

BONK

WE'VE LANDED! WE'RE THE FIRST ONES TO EVER SET FOOT ON ANOTHER PLANET! WHAT A HISTORIC MOMENT!

I STILL CAN'T BELIEVE YOU FORGOT THE CAMERA.

*I* REMEMBERED IT. *YOU* JUST DIDN'T WANT TO TURN AROUND.

SEE ANY SIGNS OF MARTIAN LIFE?

NOT YET...

HEY, LOOK! IT'S THE OLD "VIKING" SPACECRAFT THAT LANDED HERE IN THE '70s!

GOSH, I WONDER IF IT'S STILL WORKING.

BLAHHHH HOOP HOOP BOOLA ACKACKACK BOOLA

*THAT* OUGHT TO BLOW SOME CIRCUITS AT NASA!

HEE HEE HEE! I'VE ALWAYS WANTED TO DO SOMETHING LIKE THAT.

WELL, THIS IS OUR NEW HOME. I GUESS WE SHOULD UNPACK AND SET UP CAMP.

COMIC BOOKS... COMIC BOOKS... TUNA... SOME CANDY BARS... MORE TUNA... TOOTHBRUSHES... A CAN OPENER... LOOKS LIKE WE'RE ALL SET.

WHAT'S THIS?

A NIGHT LIGHT. I THOUGHT IT MIGHT BE SCARY SLEEPING ON A NEW PLANET.

BOY, YOU THOUGHT OF EVERYTHING.

NOW WE HAVE TO FIND AN OUTLET.

YEP, MARS MAY BE A LITTLE DULL, BUT IT'S BETTER THAN EARTH.

CRUNCH CRUNCH

WE'VE GOT A WHOLE PLANET TO OURSELVES. BRAND NEW AND UNSPOILED. NO PEOPLE, NO POLLUTION.

NOTHING BUT RUGGED, NATURAL BEAUTY AS FAR AS THE EYE CAN SEE.

THAT'S NOT YOUR CANDY BAR WRAPPER OVER THERE, IS IT?

IT WAS JUST THERE A MINUTE! *I* WASN'T GOING TO LEAVE IT.

I DON'T KNOW ABOUT YOU, BUT I *LIKE* IT HERE ON MARS.

I DO TOO. IT'S VERY PEACEFUL.

NOT ONLY THAT, BUT WE DON'T HAVE **MOM** HERE TO BOSS US AROUND! NO EARLY BEDTIME, NO BATHS, NO DISGUSTING DINNERS, NO...

DID THAT ROCK JUST MOVE??

MOMMMMM.!!

OH MY GOSH, THAT ROCK MOVED! THERE'S SOMETHING UNDER IT!

IT MUST BE A MARTIAN! OH NO! OH NO! IT'S PROBABLY SOME CREEPY, TENTACLED, BUG-EYED MONSTER!

YOU'RE RIGHT! THERE'S A TENTACLE NOW!

IT'S COMING OUT! WHAT WILL WE DO?!

AAUGHHHHH

IS THE MARTIAN STILL OUT THERE?

I'LL TAKE A PEEK.

I DON'T SEE HIM. HE MUST HAVE HIDDEN.

HIDDEN?? DO YOU THINK HE'S SCARED OF US?

WHY NOT? WE'RE SCARED OF HIM.

YEAH, BUT WE'RE JUST ORDINARY EARTHLINGS, NOT WEIRDOS FROM ANOTHER PLANET, LIKE HE IS.

WHY DO YOU THINK THE MARTIAN HID FROM US?

MAYBE MARTIANS DON'T LIKE EARTHLINGS.

DON'T LIKE US?! WHAT'S NOT TO LIKE?? THERE'S NOTHING WRONG WITH HUMANS!

HEY, YOU MARTIAN! COME ON OUT! WE'RE NOT BAD! WE JUST CAME HERE BECAUSE PEOPLE POLLUTED OUR OWN PLANET SO MUCH THAT... UH.. WHAT I MEAN, IS... UM...

SO WHAT ARE YOU SAYING? THAT OUR REPUTATION PRECEDED US?

WOULD YOU WELCOME IN A DOG THAT WASN'T HOUSE-TRAINED?

FOR SHOW AND TELL, I BROUGHT A SPACE ALIEN I CAPTURED IN MY BACK YARD.

YES, FOR THE LAST TWO DAYS I'VE BEEN KEEPING IT IN THIS SPECIAL ZARNIUM-COATED BAG, AND FEEDING IT PURE AMMONIA!

AND NOW, THE MOMENT YOU'VE ALL BEEN WAITING FOR!

AARGH

HOW'D IT WORK?

MY TEACHER SAYS MOM AND DAD BOTH HAVE TO SIGN MY REPORT CARDS THIS YEAR.

SCOOTCH SCOOTCH

GREETINGS. I AM AN X-387 ROBOT PROBE SENT FROM JUPITER.

MM HMM.

MY SENSORS INDICATE TRACE AMOUNTS OF CHOCOLATE IN THE PANTRY. PLEASE LOAD SOME IN MY SCOOP FOR ANALYSIS.

NO, YOU'LL SPOIL YOUR APPETITE.

MY MISSION MUST NOT FAIL. PREPARE FOR ANNIHILATION, PITIFUL EARTH FEMALE.

GO BACK TO JUPITER, X-3 WHATEVER.

YOU KNOW, WHEN YOU THINK ABOUT IT, OUR LIVES ARE PRETTY NICE.

A LOT OF KIDS DON'T HAVE AS GOOD OF A HOME LIFE AS WE DO. WE REALLY CAN'T COMPLAIN.

..WHICH ISN'T TO SAY WE SHOULD GO HOME YET.

WHEN DO YOU THINK THEY'LL SEE THE CAR WINDSHIELD?

HI SUSIE! GUESS WHAT I BROUGHT FOR LUNCH.

NO! GO SIT BY SOMEONE ELSE, OK? YOU ALWAYS SAY YOUR LUNCH IS SOMETHING REVOLTING, AND I DON'T WANT TO HEAR IT!

GEE WHIZ, WHAT'S WRONG WITH YOU? MY LUNCH IS PEANUT BUTTER. WHAT'S SO DISGUSTING ABOUT THAT?!

HMPH. I'M GLAD THAT ONE DAY OUT OF THE YEAR YOU CAN BE CIVIL.

IT'S MY *DESSERT* THAT'S GROSS! LOOK, A THERMOS FULL OF PHLEGM!

CALVIN, WILL YOU RUN AND GET MY PURSE, PLEASE? I NEED THE CALCULATOR.

SURE.

HERE YOU ARE.

THANKS.

AHEM.

I'M NOT GOING TO TIP YOU!!

HUH! SEE IF I EVER FETCH ANYTHING AGAIN.

ELECTION DAY IS **COMING UP,** DAD. PEOPLE WANT TO KNOW WHERE YOU STAND ON THE ISSUES.

SUCH AS?

LATER BEDTIMES, EXPANDED TV PRIVILEGES, SHORTER SCHOOL WEEKS, AND LESS DISCIPLINE.

I'M AGAINST THEM ALL.

I SEE.

HOW'S YOUR IRA? PRETTY WELL FUNDED?

GO TO BED.

I THINK THE WORST OF THIS IS OVER, SO JUST TRY TO GET SOME SLEEP.

I'M GOING BACK TO BED, BUT GIVE ME A CALL IF YOU FEEL SICK AGAIN, OK? NOW GET SOME REST.

MM HMM.

POOR LITTLE KID.

YECCHHH! THERE IS NOTHING WORSE THAN A SICK ROOMMATE! FACE THAT WAY!

IT'S SCARY BEING SICK... ESPECIALLY AT NIGHT.

WHAT IF SOMETHING IS REALLY WRONG WITH ME, AND I HAVE TO GO TO THE HOSPITAL??

WHAT IF THEY STICK ME FULL OF TUBES AND HOSES? WHAT IF THEY HAVE TO OPERATE? WHAT IF THE OPERATION FAILS? WHAT IF THIS IS MY... MY... LAST NIGHT... ALIVE??

THEN I CAN LOOK FORWARD TO HAVING THE BED TO MYSELF TOMORROW.

FEW THINGS ARE LESS COMFORTING THAN A TIGER WHO'S UP TOO LATE.

FEELING ANY BETTER THIS MORNING, CALVIN?

NO.

I GUESS I'D BETTER MAKE YOU AN APPOINTMENT WITH THE DOCTOR.

OK.

IT'S SATURDAY, BY THE WAY. YOU WON'T MISS SCHOOL.

I KNOW.

WELL, IT LOOKS LIKE CALVIN JUST CAUGHT THE BUG GOING AROUND. NOTHING SERIOUS.

KEEP AN EYE ON HIM, AND LET ME KNOW IF HE ISN'T FEELING BETTER SOON.

OK. THANK YOU.

SO LONG, CALVIN. YOU WERE A GOOD PATIENT THIS TIME.

MM.

NOTHING LIKE A LITTLE VIRUS TO TAKE THE EDGE OFF A KID.

I'D STILL RATHER LET HIS TEACHER DEAL WITH HIM.

I GET TO STAY HOME FROM SCHOOL TODAY.

I GET TO LIE IN BED, DRINK TEA, AND READ COMIC BOOKS ALL DAY.

I WISH I COULD DO THIS EVERY DAY.

...LIKE SOME PEOPLE I KNOW.

YOUR MOM DOESN'T BRING *ME* TEA IN BED.

I WANT SOME MORE TOAST.

ROOM SERVICE!!

HA! *THAT* SURE GOT YOU UP HERE QUICK!

TOMORROW YOU'RE GOING TO SCHOOL.

I THINK PEOPLE WORRY TOO MUCH ABOUT LITTLE THINGS.

ALL THEY DO IS MAKE THEMSELVES UNHAPPY THAT WAY.

WHY GET AN ULCER OVER THINGS THAT DON'T REALLY MATTER?

LIKE THE BOOK REPORT YOU'RE SUPPOSED TO BE WRITING NOW ON THE BOOK YOU HAVEN'T READ?

EXACTLY. CASE IN POINT.

WHY IN THE WORLD AM I WAITING IN THE POURING RAIN FOR THE SCHOOL BUS TO TAKE ME SOMEWHERE I DON'T EVEN WANT TO GO?

I GO TO SCHOOL, BUT I NEVER LEARN WHAT I WANT TO KNOW.

I HATE SCHOOL.

EACH DAY I COUNT THE HOURS UNTIL SCHOOL'S OVER. THEN I COUNT THE DAYS UNTIL THE WEEKEND. THEN I COUNT THE WEEKS UNTIL THE MONTH IS OVER, AND THEN THE MONTHS UNTIL SUMMER.

I ALWAYS HAVE TO POSTPONE WHAT I *WANT* TO DO FOR WHAT I *HAVE* TO DO!

WELCOME TO THE WORLD.

WOULD YOU SIGN THIS PARENTAL EXCUSE TO GET ME OUT OF THE NEXT 11½ YEARS OF SCHOOL?

# Calvin and Hobbes

by WATTERSON

THE VALIANT SPACEMAN SPIFF, INTERGALACTIC EXPLORER, COMES IN OVER THE MOUNTAINS OF A STRANGE PLANET!

OUR HERO DESPERATELY HOPES TO FIND A REST AREA WITH WORKING FACILITIES.

SPACEMAN SPIFF LANDS ON THE DISTANT PLANET ZOKK!

CLIMBING DOWN FROM HIS SPACECRAFT, OUR HERO PREPARES TO EXPLORE THE SURFACE!

UNEXPECTEDLY, SPIFF'S FIRST STEP SENDS HIM CAREENING THROUGH THE SKY!

SPIFF QUICKLY REALIZES THAT PLANET ZOKK HAS ONLY A FRACTION OF EARTH'S GRAVITY!

OOF

WITH PRACTICE, OUR HERO SOON FINDS HE CAN BOUND EFFORTLESSLY ACROSS THE LANDSCAPE!

WATTERSON

STOP BOUNCING ON THE BED AND GO TO SLEEP!

DUMB BALLOON.

POOF POOF

POOF POOOF

POOFF

HEY, SUSIE, DID YOU HAVE ANY TROUBLE WITH OUR MATH HOMEWORK LAST NIGHT?

NO, WHY?

I THOUGHT A COUPLE OF THESE WERE TRICKY. CAN I CHECK MY ANSWERS WITH YOURS?

OK.

THANKS. WHAT DID YOU GET FOR QUESTION ONE?

SEVEN.

SEVEN? GOOD, THAT'S WHAT I GOT. WHAT DID YOU GET FOR QUESTION TWO?

DROP DEAD, CALVIN.

EVER SIT AND WATCH ANTS?

LOOK AT THIS ONE. HE'S CARRYING A CRUMB THAT'S BIGGER THAN HE IS, AND HE'S *RUNNING*.

AND IF YOU PUT AN OBSTACLE IN FRONT OF HIM, HE'LL SCRAMBLE LIKE CRAZY UNTIL HE GETS ACROSS IT. HE DOESN'T LET ANYTHING STOP HIM.

I JUST CAN'T IDENTIFY WITH THAT KIND OF WORK ETHIC.

# Calvin and Hobbes

by WATTERSON

I FEEL A BIG SNEEZE WELLING UP.

...WHICH IS ALWAYS A SURE SIGN THAT I'M NOT CARRYING A HANDKERCHIEF.

AH...AH...AH..

CHOOOOO!

MOM, I SNEEZED AND BLEW MY HEAD OFF!

PULL YOUR SHIRT DOWN, CALVIN. YOU'RE NOT FOOLING ANYONE.

MOM WOULD BE A LOT MORE FUN IF SHE WAS A LITTLE MORE GULLIBLE.

# CaLViN and HobbEs

by WATTERSON

RINGGG

WHAT A DAY.

YOU THINK THAT'S FUNNY? COME BACK AND FIGHT, YOU WEASEL!

WHAT HAPPENED TO *YOU*??

DON'T ASK. I'M GOING UPSTAIRS TO CHANGE.

CALVIN'S ROOM • ENTER & DIE

NOT AGAAINN.

WHERE'S CALVIN?

I SENT HIM TO HIS ROOM. I CAUGHT HIM MAKING PRANK CALLS TO PET STORES, ASKING IF THEY'D BUY HIS TIGER.

HEY, SUSIE, CAN I BORROW YOUR BLACK CRAYON?

OK, BUT DON'T BREAK IT, AND DON'T PEEL THE PAPER OFF, AND COLOR WITH ALL SIDES OF IT SO IT STAYS POINTY.

GEEZ, WHY DON'T YOU TAKE OUT AN INSURANCE POLICY ON IT?

JUST DON'T RUIN MY CRAYON. WHAT ARE YOU DRAWING ANYWAY?

BLACK BEARS ATTACKING A BLACK FOREST CAMPGROUND AT MIDNIGHT.

GIVE ME MY CRAYON BACK.

HEY! WHAT'S THIS STUFF IN MY SOUP?! YECCHH! IS THIS RICE?!? IT HAD BETTER *NOT* BE!

RICE? LET ME SEE.

LOOK! THESE LITTLE WHITE THINGS! SEE, THERE'S RICE IN MY SOUP! I HATE RICE!

I DIDN'T PUT ANY RICE IN. THOSE ARE MAGGOTS.

EWWWW!

ANOTHER LOVELY MEAL AT HOME WITH MY FAMILY. ...I WISH MY JOB REQUIRED MORE TRAVEL.

WELL, HE'S *EATING* IT NOW, RIGHT?

GOSH, WAIT 'TIL I TELL EVERYONE AT SCHOOL WHAT *WE* HAD FOR DINNER!

UH OH.

HOOP

EEP!

I'VE GOT THE HICCUPS SOMETHING TERRIBLE, MOM.

DRINK SOME WATER.

WHEN I GROW UP, I WANT TO BE AN INVENTOR. FIRST I WILL INVENT A TIME MACHINE.

THEN I'LL COME BACK TO YESTERDAY

AND TAKE MYSELF TO TOMORROW

AND SKIP THIS DUMB ASSIGNMENT.

MOMMM, I'M HOME FROM SCHOOL! OPEN THE DOOR FOR ME, OK?

WHAT'S THE MATTER? IT WASN'T LOCKED.

SOMETIMES HOBBES IS WAITING TO POUNCE ON ME AS SOON AS I OPEN THE DOOR.

OH FOR HEAVEN'S SAKE! FROM NOW ON, DON'T CALL ME TO COME TO THE DOOR UNLESS IT'S LOCKED.

HA! I SURE OUT-SMARTED HOBBES *THIS* TIME!

THBBPTT!

SISSY.

BOY, I'M IN A BAD MOOD TODAY! EVERYONE HAD BETTER STEER CLEAR OF ME!

I HATE *EVERYBODY!* AS FAR AS I'M CONCERNED, EVERYONE ON THE PLANET CAN JUST DROP DEAD. PEOPLE ARE SCUM.

WELL-L-L? DOESN'T ANYONE WANT TO CHEER ME UP?!?

GET OUT OF MY WAY! I'M IN A BAD MOOD!

?

!

I'LL BET A PET DOG WOULD'VE GOTTEN OUT OF MY WAY.

WATCH OUT, MOM. I'M IN A BAD MOOD.

BE IN A BAD MOOD SOMEWHERE ELSE, OK? I'M BUSY.

HMPH! I'LL BET MY *BIOLOGICAL* MOTHER WOULD'VE BOUGHT ME A COMIC BOOK AND MADE ME FEEL BETTER INSTEAD OF SHUNNING ME LIKE *YOU*.

KID, ANYONE *BUT* YOUR BIOLOGICAL MOTHER WOULD'VE LEFT YOU TO THE WOLVES LONG AGO.

YEAH, RIGHT. REALLY, HOW MUCH DID YOU PAY FOR ME?

WHAT'S YOUR TAIL FOR?

MY TAIL?

YEAH. WHY DO TIGERS NEED TAILS?

GEE, I'M NOT REALLY SURE.

I GUESS JUST BECAUSE THEY LOOK GOOD.

SO IT'S SORT OF A NECKTIE FOR YOUR BUTT?

LET'S NOT BE VULGAR. YOU'RE JUST JEALOUS.

The End